# Meditation~ Sense Faculty

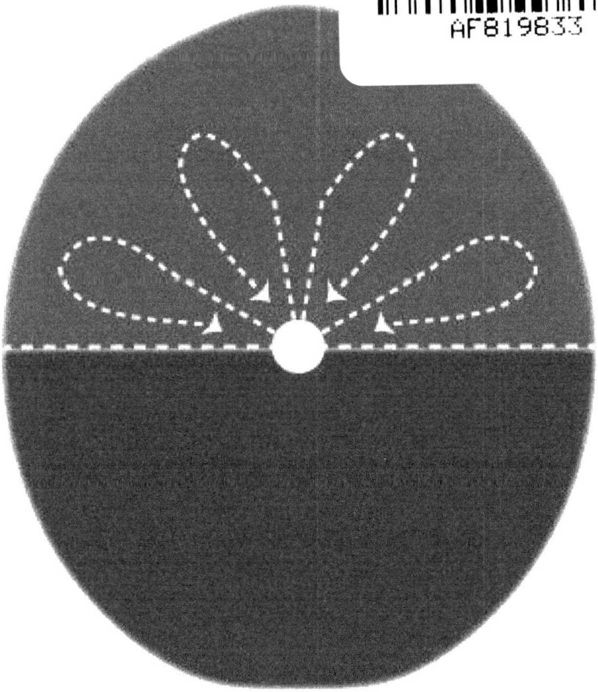



*Michael Beloved ~ devaPriyā Yoginī*

**Correspondence:**

Michael Beloved
19311 SW 30TH ST
Miramar FL 33029
axisnexus@gmail.com

devaPriya Yogini
7211 41ST Court East
Sarasota FL 34243
devapriyayogini@gmail.com

**ISBN**

**9781942887034**

**LCCN**

**2016903460**

# Table of Contents

# *Introduction*

The original draft was written by devaPriya Yogini after Michael suggested that a book be composed which could inspire sense orb discovery. The manuscript was titled *Sense Orb Discovery*. Later when it was reviewed by Michael, he changed the title to *Meditation ~ Sense Faculty*. The objective of this practice is to discover the sensual orbs in the subtle body, but that is a tall order. We toned down the title for the realization of what we know as sense faculties.

There is a hurdle in this meditation because of the abstraction in the mental and emotional interplay in the psyche. If the yogi or yogini is courageous, he or she will not be scared of this subtlety, and will tolerate it while continuing the exercises and suggestions herein.

The achievement is to realize that the sense faculties have a subtle version which we should discover and use to realize what the subtle body is and how to operate it for our convenience. These exercises and suggestions should be remembered. Then over time when one meditates, one will use them. One will practice some of the techniques on the basis of our suggestions which penetrate into the subconscious and serve as prompts and motivations.

Each of these ideas were tested by Michael personally. He used them recently just to be sure that they are fruitful in the present era. These yield a confidence which is necessary in the effort to switch from physical reference to subtle focus. Nature robbed us of any subtle perception we had before taking the physical body. To regain our foothold in the subtle terrain before death of the physical body, we should turret the focus away from the physical and bravely embrace what is abstract but what is real nevertheless.

# Chapter 1

# Special Diagrams

These were developed by devaPriya Yogini.

## *Sense Orb*

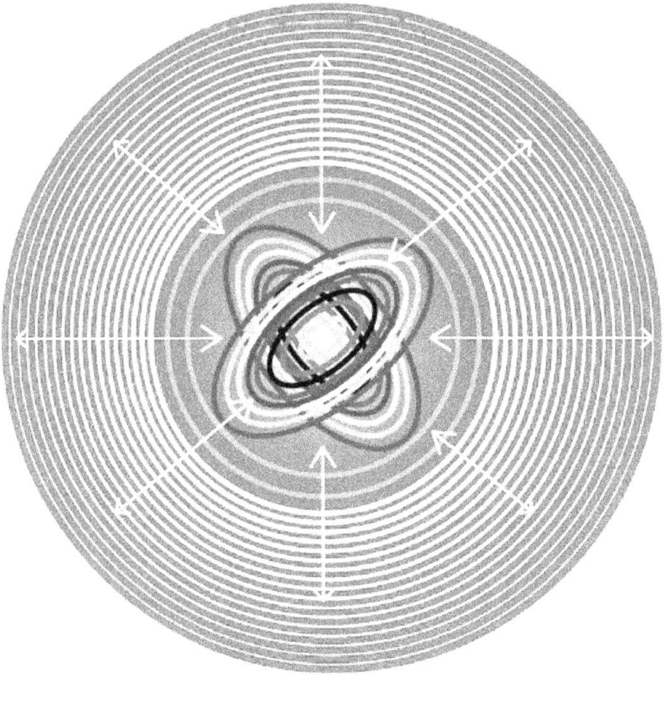

# *Potent Attention Ray*

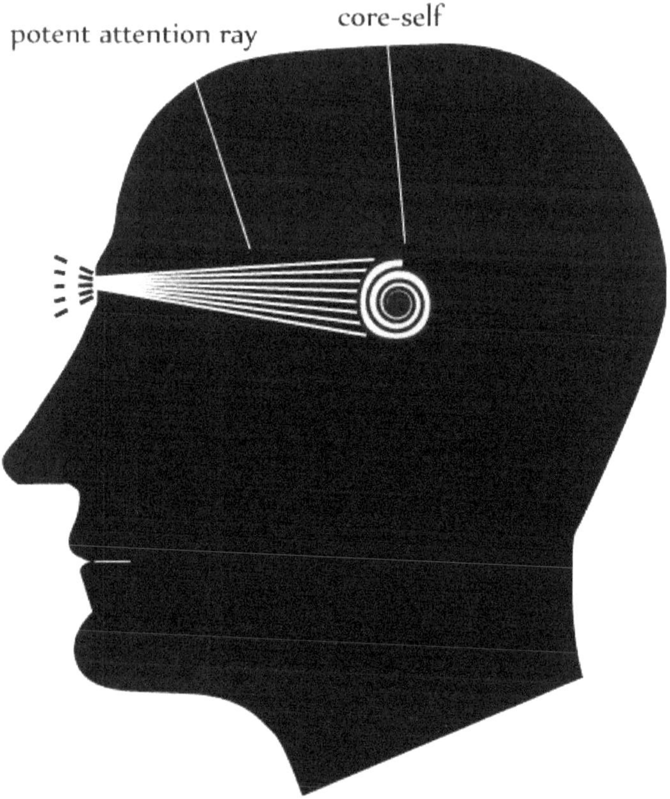

# *Smell Sense Faculty*

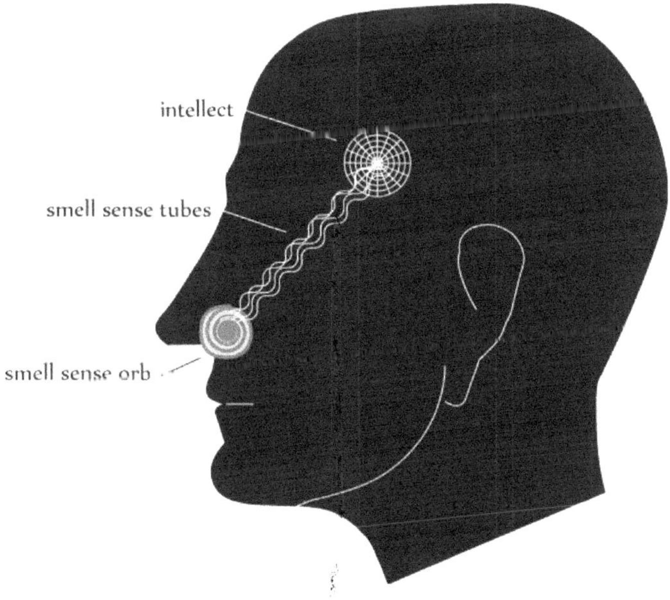

## *Smell Orb Energy Tubes*

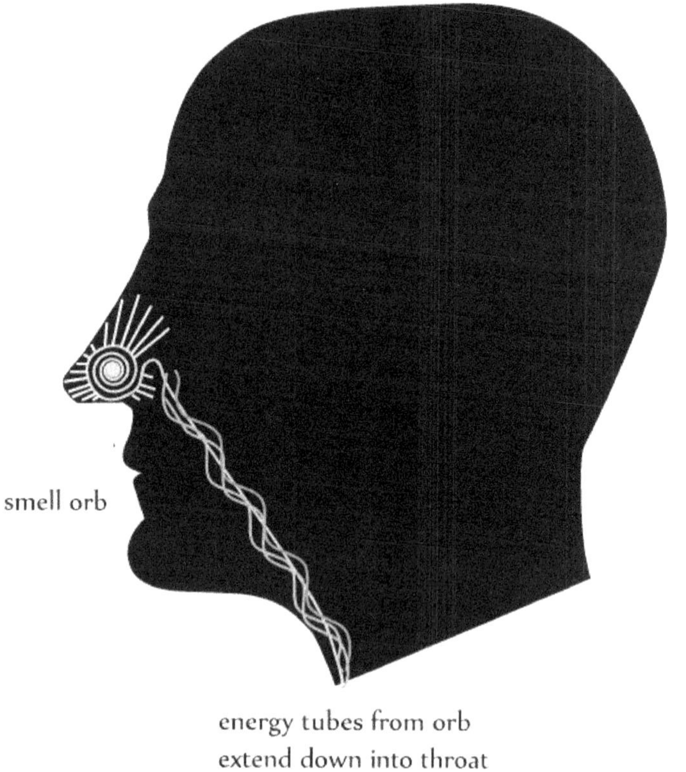

## *Sense Orb Radiation*

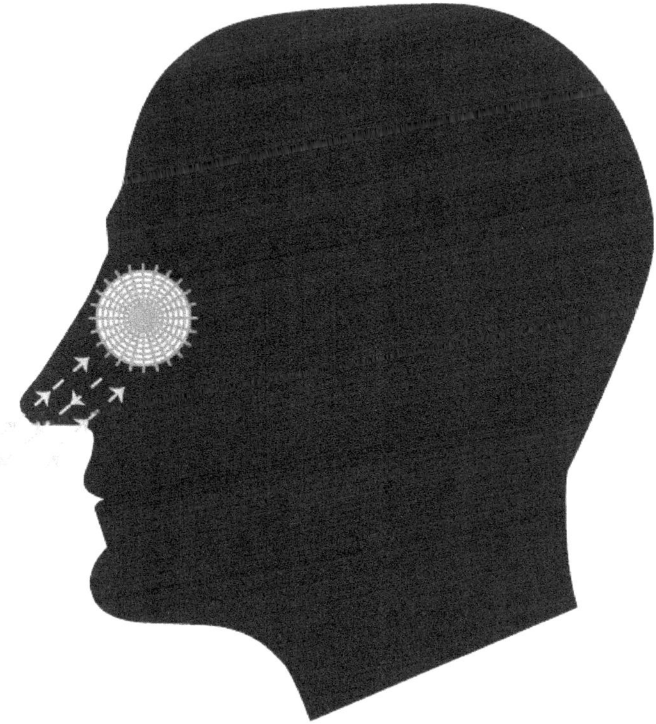

sense orb radiating energy outward and inward

## *Taste Sense Faculty*

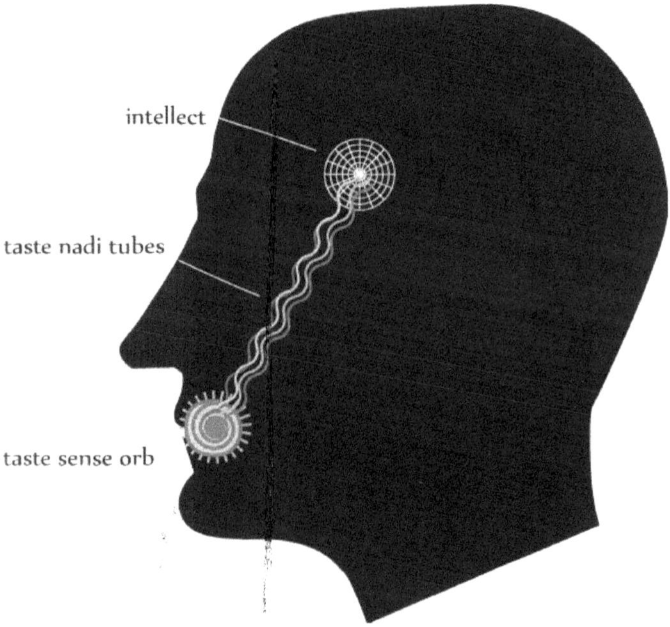

## *Taste Orb*

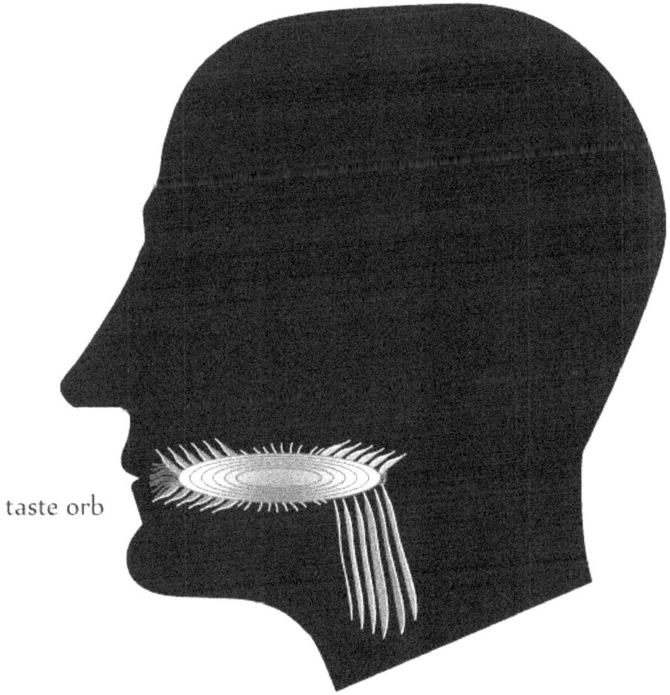


subtle sense energy flows through tongue, teeth, gums, jaws, throat and lips.
disc shaped orb sits horizontally in the mouth

# *Visual Sense Orb*

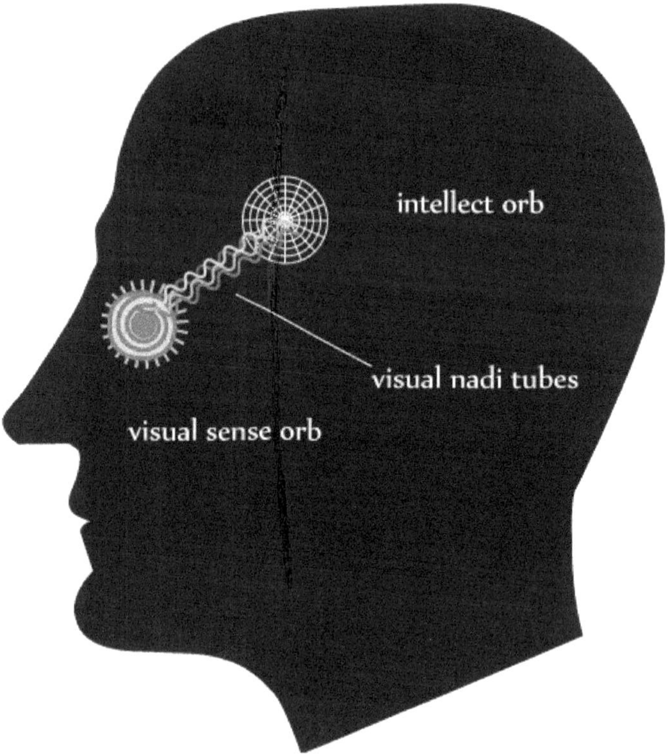

# *Vision Bubble Orb*

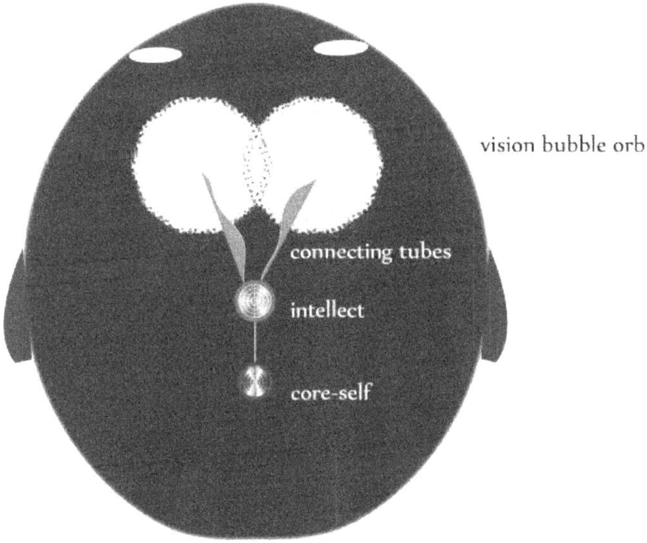

## *Touch Sense Faculty*

touch sense diagram

(skin nadis) subtle tubes originating
at all points of skin, inserting in intellect orb

## *Hearing Sense*

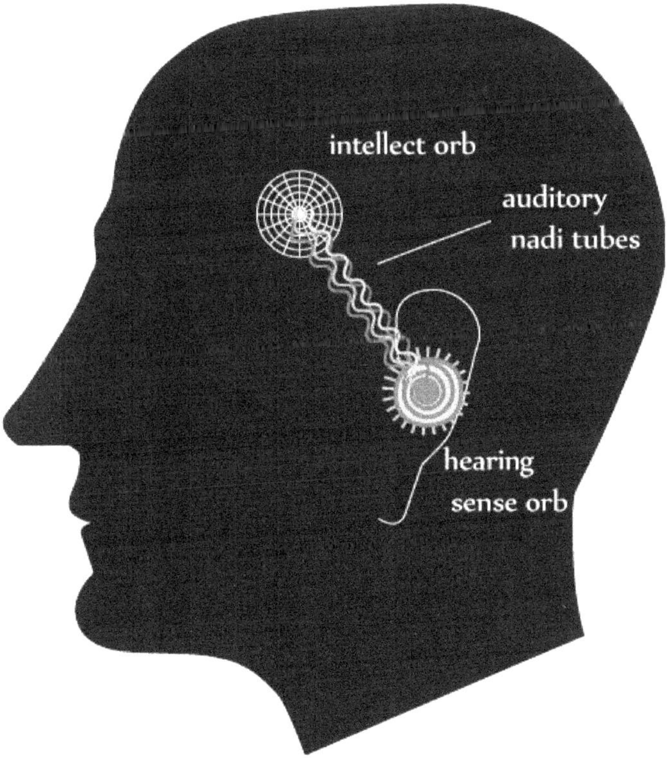

## *Hearing Sense Orbs*

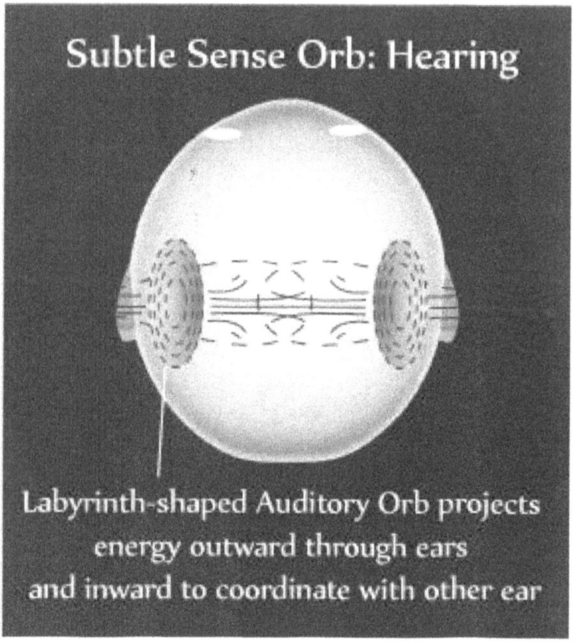

# *Hearing Sense Orbs Communication*

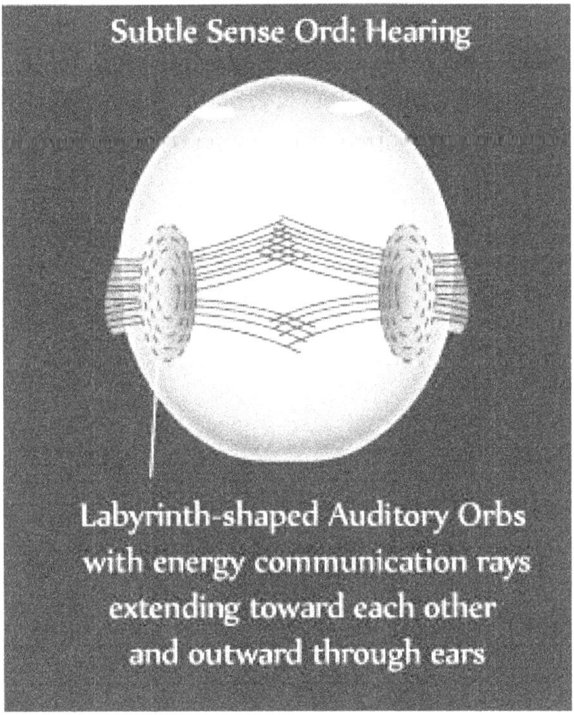

# *Senses Alert*

Senses Alert

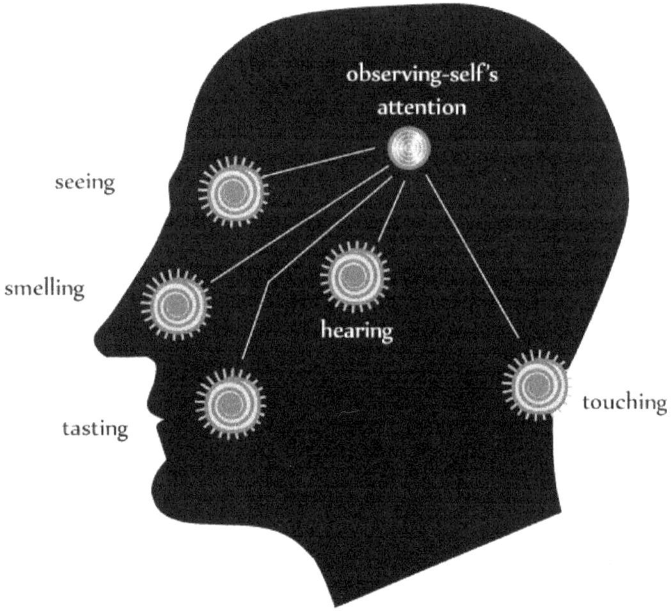


Energy from the observing-self flows abundantly through the subtle sense orbs

# Chapter 2 Observing-Self as Reference

The co-authors agreed that there should be a reference from which a yogi or yogini would discover and study each of the sense faculties. We agreed that it should be the default position of the core-self. In a sense wherever that core-self usually resides as its default location, is the core-self. This is not true of course but for the purpose of this book, we ask you to assume that this is true. Take for granted that the location of the core-self is the core-self even though in fact the location of an object, even a psychic or spiritual one, is not the object itself.

In mystic studies, one may begin with assumptions and with erroneous ideas and misconstrued perceptions. From there one may progress to get clarity step by step. The embryo is not the mother. The mother is not the embryo. Yet in the practical sense, they move together as one unit. It works for the time being, for at least nine month's period to consider them to be one and the same. Initially it serves the purpose to consider the default location of the core-self to be the core-self. Later when the meditation becomes proficient, we may change that view.

Some mystics claim that the default location of the core-self is the heart area. Others says that it is the center of the chest as contrasted to the heart which leans away from center to the left side of the body. There is support for this in some writings of reputed mystics. It is written in the

Vedic literatures that there is a Lord in the heart which is Krishna or Vishnu. Some say that the Lord in the heart is the higher self of the self. You should determine what for you will be the default location of *you*, as the observing-self. Whatever you decide please substitute that as the reference from which to do these practices.

However, we suggest, and it is our view, that the default location of the core-self is the existential center of the subtle head.

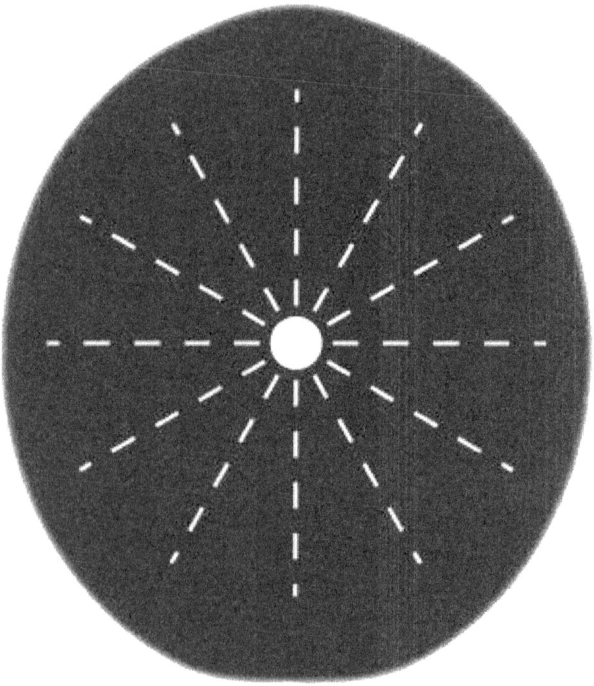

We consider the mental faculties in combination with the emotional ones to be the prime reference. Suppose we agree with those who say that the heart, or the center of the chest, is the ultimate location of the core-self, then in that case, we ask that for the practice in this book, they should use the center of the head as the reference. This is because thinking takes place in the head of the subtle body. It does not take place in the centralized radial for emotional feelings. Thus for those who attest to the heart or central chest as the self's default location, we ask them to switch to the location from where thinking and ideation is observed.

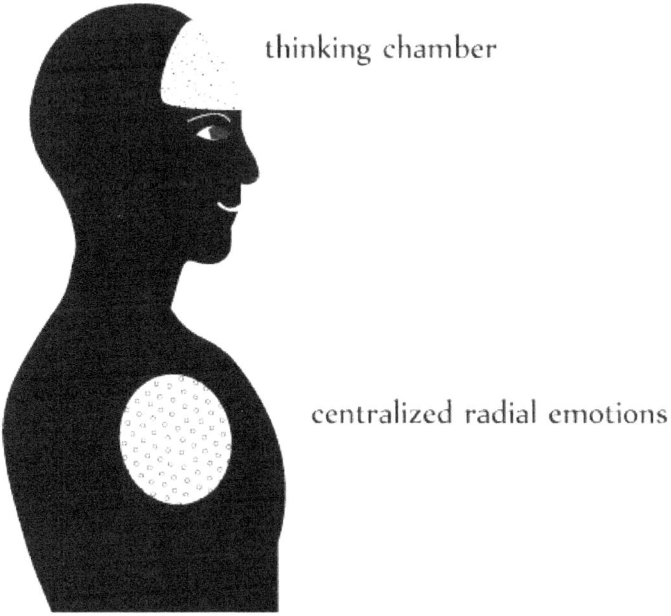


We must first establish this reference location in the existential center of the subtle head. You should not try to physically determine where this location is. Use your feelings, those in the head of the subtle body to go to the center of head awareness as you feel it, with your eyes closed and your attention kept within the skull.

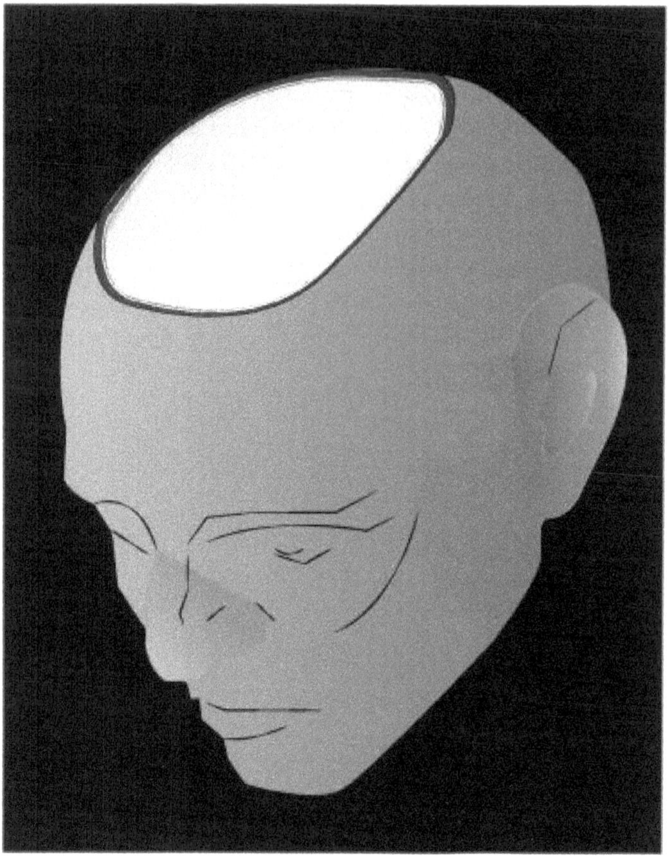

If a question arises as to what is the subtle head. That is answered simply. It is the same physical head but it is specifically the awareness which is contained in that space. From now on when we mention subtle head, just think that we mean the awareness in the physical head when the eyes are closed.

To complete this book, it is required that you be quite familiar with the subtle head and especially with the central location where the observing-self is positioned when it is entertained by thoughts and images in the mind. The mental convention is that the observing-self ignores and neglects its importance, when it is entertained by thoughts and images. We need to meditate on this central self to change the relation which it has with the thoughts and images. Instead of always being preoccupied with mental scenes and sounds, this practice requires that the observing-self, the *you*, the *I*, should turn to observe itself, leaving aside the mental and emotional constructions of the mind.

We are not concerned with denying the ego or with finding a higher self. We are concerned only with the observing-self which in the mind, sees, hears and feels, ideas, impressions, images, sounds and other mental media.

Is this self faulty?

Is this self an illusion?

Here we are not concerned to answer these questions. To complete this research into the abstract actions in the sense faculties, we will operate as that observing-self.

Please practice a meditation daily such that as soon as you sit in silence to meditate you are anchored automatically in the awareness-center of the subtle head. Usually this observing-self is exactly what it is, which is that it is an observer of what takes place in the mind. Even what takes place externally in the physical world is indirectly perceived in the mind in a parallel configuration of the re-constructed events. That is seen by this observing-self as a photocopy of what actually happened. This is one reason why some say that whatever takes place in the mind is illusion. Let us however not discuss that issue in this practice because whatever you read here from paper or screen or whatever you hear from a speaker or sound system from this book, is a reproduction of the original manuscript and is valid in so far as it reproduces that original.

This observing-self, the perceiver, is accustomed to being entertained but we must change this function of the self to complete the practices in this book. Instead of being entertained, this self should turn about so that its attention is on itself. The attention should be lifted from the machinations of the mind and be placed on the self. The observer should observe itself. The attention which leaves the self and goes out into the mind searching for ideas, images, sounds and whatever the mind constructs, should if it must leave the self, make a loop and return to the self without scanning the mind space for images and ideas, without lingering to observe images and ideas.

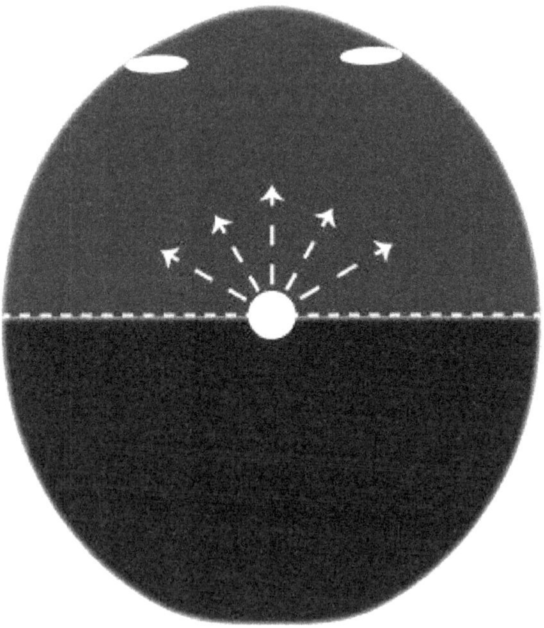

attention searches the mind for ideas

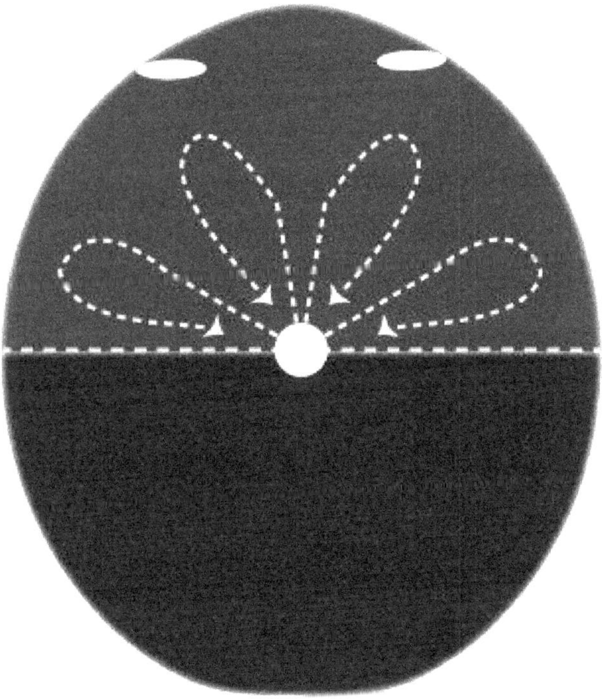

attention leaves the observing-self
and loops back to that self

Day after day, sit to meditate while situating the attention of the self into the self. Resist the urge to secure interest in the ideas which are displayed in the mind. Practice this repeatedly until it becomes your natural state in meditation, until no effort is required to have this happen, until the mind's natural state is for the observing-self to be self-focused with its interest either not leaving the self or with it leaving and immediately looping back to the self, leaving aside the theatrics of the mind's idea constructions.

psyche enclosure
with glow of observing-self
in head space

The observing-self is the factor which notes or is entertained by the mental and emotional constructions in the mind. Some say this self is an illusion. Some attest to it as being the individual limited entity. Some say that it is the confused potential supreme self which will reclaim itself as being the Absolute. For the meditations herein please regard this self as the reference.

Our terminology is such that we avoid using the term self for the observing-self. We want to assign self to being the entire psychological system in which the observing-self is a part only. In our usage self is psyche, the entire composite consciousness of one person.

In the case of a pregnant mammal, the embryo which develops within that adult psyche is the psyche of another being which invaded the female mammal, grew within it and then was evicted from it. The pregnant mammal has two psyches; that of the mother and the offspring. Please read this paragraph again so that you understand how we use the terms self, observing-self and psyche. Note that for this book, observing-self is not the conventional self but is a part of the self, with the self being the psyche which contains the observing-self and other factors.

The observing-self switches back and forth through one of three states. These are

- Out-focus
- In-focus
- Non-focus

For this practice, you are required to study the observing-self in each of these states. You should also study how it switches or is switched through these three states. Look at the diagrams and explanations:

## *Out-focus:*

Out-focus is the convention of the mind which is to range for sense objects in the external world. It hashes over the ideas which it gains when relating to the said objects. This is the extrovert state of mind which is awarded to most creatures in the material world. It does not require much endeavor and for that matter it is mostly a spontaneous operation. To complete the lessons in this book, this nature-awarded extrovert faculty should be restrained. Its spontaneous process should be minutely observed so that the observing-self may understand its energy shifts and operations.

In order to find the reference, which we assigned as the observing-self in its default location in the head space, you should begin at the place where you spontaneously become involved with this out-focus, either looking into the mind to see its constructions or looking through the senses to grasp something in the physical environment which is outside of your body.

First observe the drawing power, the pushing or pulling force, of this out-focus. Make an effort to stop its outward energy flow. Notice its strength which is like a taut muscle or a spring-loaded high-tension wire.

Wear a blindfold. With eyes closed, sit with stillness.

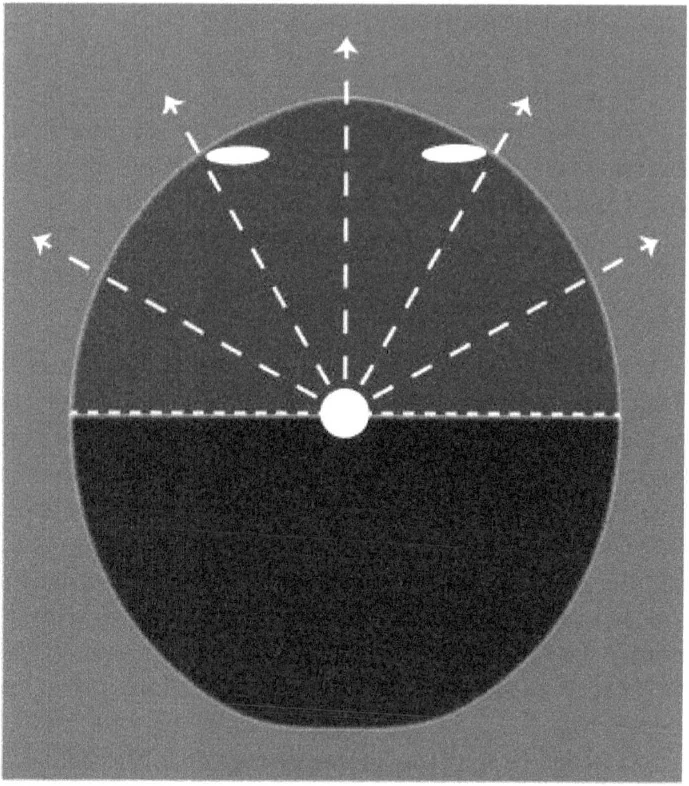

out-focus to objects outside the mind

Feel the energy going outward through the skull into the external environment.

Feel and distinguish the energy which remains in the head and compulsively focuses on thoughts, even trivial and imaginary ones.

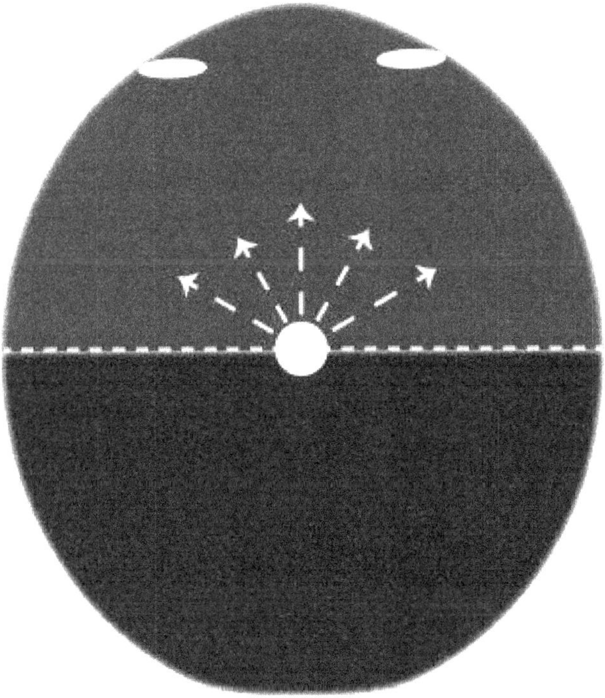

out-focus within the mind

Notice how long it takes to release interest in thoughts. Notice! Even though you use a blindfold, and have intentions to meditate, you still feel the urge to remove the blindfold, open the eyelids and investigate sense objects which you smelled, touched or heard.

What is the process of these commands? How does the sensual energy transit to objects outside the psyche?

How does the mind reach conclusions about detected objects?

How does the observing-self decide to pursue or not to pursue an object?

Is the observing-self influenced by other factors in the psyche (self)?

Can the observing-self retrieve its interest from the outward-going energy and have no regrets for non-participation?

Is it dependent on this involvement?

## *Source of out-focus interest*

At first you should merely observe the pull of your interest into thoughts which are generated impulsively by the mind. Once you do that sufficiently where you know that those thoughts, their pulling interest, and you as the observing-self, are distinct factors, you should silently notice the origin of the pulling force.

Is this force being pulled?

Or is it being ushered into the thoughts or into the pursuit of an external object? In the case of a magnet and iron, when the two are in proximity, they may both move towards each other.

Is the magnet pulled to the iron?

Is the iron pulled to the magnet?

Or is it a mutual attraction where an equal force is expressed in either case?

At first it will be near impossible to explain what happens in the pulling of energy through the mind towards thoughts and the pulling of the energy through the skull into the external environment. However in time, when this meditation is done frequently, it will be evident that the energy which is pulled comes from the observing self. The evidence for this is realized when the self experiences that if perchance it loses interest in the thought object or external object, the pulling force collapses immediately, even though it seems to make a counter effort to reestablish the attraction.

Suppose for instance when there is iron which is attracted to a magnet, the iron loses interest in the magnet or becomes oblivious of it, and then we find that the pulling force of the magnet collapses but begins again as soon as the iron develops new interest. That would be like the relationship between the observing-self and a thought or the observing-self and an object which is outside the psyche.

The observing-self is the focus of the out-focus but that is difficult to perceive because it seems in reality that the observing-self becomes focused on something other than itself, or that it becomes interested in something or someone else. This paradox is solved in meditation, through clarity in discerning detailed events in the mind space.

The pull of the observing self, is really a pull of its interest. The thought-energy or the external object wants to gain the interest of the observing-self because it wants to pull energy from that observer. This pull forms a focus on the observing self, such that the observer feels the need, feels compelled, to focus on thoughts in the mind or objects outside the mind. It may seem that energy of the thoughts come from the thoughts and certainly some energy does emanate from the thoughts or from the objects which the self is attracted to, but the compulsion in that energy is actually a need in the thought-formation or in the external object for the self to make the observation.

After meditating repeatedly and observing the sequence of events in an attraction to thoughts and objects, the observing-self sees that even though there is energy which comes from the thoughts and objects, still that energy is an inducement for the observing-self to make itself the focus of the thoughts or objects.

The thoughts and objects need the interest-energy of the self. Their outward reach of energy is an inducement for the self to invest its attention and remain as the focus of whatever takes place. Of course this a compounded situation because in any circumstance there may be more than one observing self, some using human bodies and some using lower animal forms. Even vegetation may be involved in this complexity.

## *In-focus*

In-focus is the folding-in of the interest of the self. It is a developed practice in meditation which is called pratyahar sensual energy withdrawal. It was mentioned by Patanjali in his Yoga Sutras and by Krishna in the Bhagavad Gita discourse. Patanjali listed it as the fifth stage of the eight-aspect ashtanga yoga process. It is the primary act before deep introspection. There is a nice analogy about this practice, given by Lord Krishna in the Bhagavad Gita:

यदा संहरते चायं
कूर्मोऽङ्गानीव सर्वशः।
इन्द्रियाणीन्द्रियार्थेभ्यस्
तस्य प्रज्ञा प्रतिष्ठिता ॥२.५८॥

yadā saṁharate cāyaṁ
kūrmo'ṅgānīva sarvaśaḥ
indriyāṇīndriyārthebhyas
tasya prajñā pratiṣṭhitā (2.58)

*yadā — when; saṁharate — pulls; cāyaṁ = ca — and + ayam — this; kūrmo = kūrmaḥ — tortoise; 'ṅgānīva = aṅgānīva = aṅgāni — limbs + iva — like, compared to; sarvaśaḥ — fully; indriyāṇīndriyārthebhyas = indriyani — senses + indriyarthebhyaḥ — attractive things; tasya — his; prajñā — reality-piercing vision; pratiṣṭhitā — is established*

**When such a person pulls fully out of moods, he or she may be compared to the tortoise with its limbs retracted. The senses are withdrawn from the attractive things in the case of a person whose reality-piercing vision is established. (Bhagavad Gita 2.58)**

This verse described the extraction of the self's interest from the world which is outside the material body. This is the elementary part of sensual energy withdrawal.

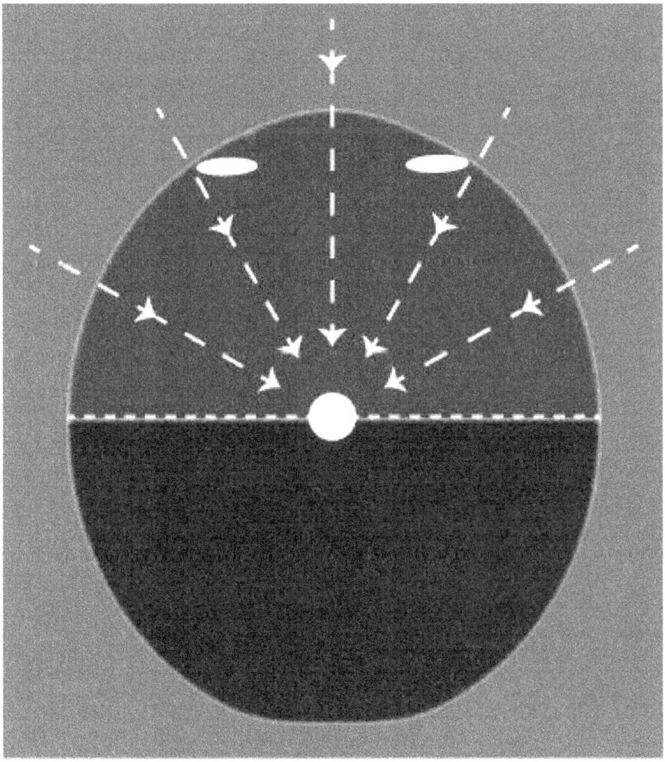

in-focus from objects outside the mind

There is yet another part which is the extraction of the interest from the thinking constructions in the mind itself. At first the yogi withdraws interest from the world which is outside his material body. Then he discovers that there are undesirable interests within the mind. He must then endeavor to pull his attention away from these undesirable

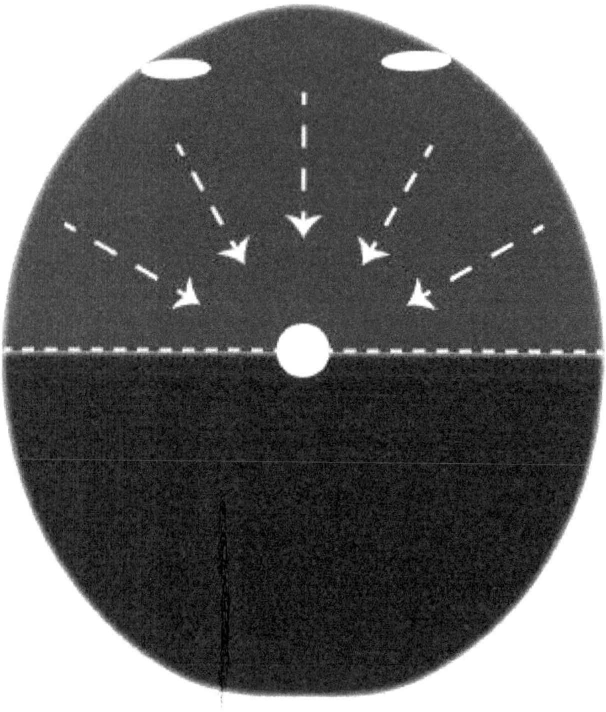

in-focus within the mind

subtle incidences. These are parts of pratyahar sensual energy withdrawal, the fifth stage of yoga.

- Sit to meditate.
- Close the eyelids.
- Withdraw interest in external smells and sounds.
- Check to see if there remains interests in external objects.

What are these interests?

Why the failure to detach from them?

Why does such external objects have the power to use your observational ability?

This practice allows the observing-self to gage its resistance to specific objects. The self may struggle to come to terms with its lack of control. It may become frustrated and disappointed with this weakness.

Slowly but surely, over a course of days, weeks, months or years, the observing-self could come to terms with itself by studying the relationship it has with this attraction to thoughts and objects.

- Sit to meditate.
- Close the eyelids.
- Withdraw interest in external smells and sounds.
- Settle in just as if you are a person who closed the blinds of his house and relaxed on a couch in his building.
- Take stock of the mental and emotional interest. Check to see what arises in the mind.
- Make an effort to terminate the operation of thinking and the memory events which bring emotional incidences from the past into mental view.

Practice this repeatedly until you master the process and can do it instantly as soon as you sit to meditate with closed eyelids.

## *In-focus as a precursor to sleep*

In-focus is rated as a partial or complete practice of the pratyahar sensual energy withdrawal stage of yoga but it does occur by the grace of nature. Please observe what happens when you sit to meditate, how your mind may at first agree to cease thought activity, but then it resumes what it really wants to do which is to either reach out to make contact with an external object, or hash over details of an incidence, or construct a video of events which requires your astute observation.

In-focus does not begin with success. It begins with failure for sure but a failure which is accompanied with observation. This observation over time leads to more and more control of what the mind can present to the observing-self and how that self will be attracted to what is presented. Over time, this observing-self will gradually increase its controlled interaction with the mind. It will take practice.

By the grace of nature, you may observe how the body/mind combination engages in a gradual or abrupt in-focus just before sleep. Sometimes before sleep, there is no attempt to in-focus. Then someone may use a chemical to induce sleep. However when the body/mind combination naturally induces asleep, you should observe how it does that. There will be a point at which you lose perception but up to that point, please note the process.

If you are extremely exhausted this will not be possible. If not you can make subtle observations. You can perceive how the sense faculties fold-in from the external world. Then they make the effort to continue fiddling with thoughts and memories. Then even this slows down until it continues so slowly that you can see the thoughts as if they were stretched, fractured or parceled beyond recognition. At this point your observational powers fail as your ability to remember is reduced to nil.

Where is the self located when in-focus is near completion?

Where is the self when it finds itself to be diminished in objectivity?

Where is it, when it disappears completely, having lost all objectivity?

Is it still at the center of the awareness in the head?

Has it relocated in the heart or chest area?

Did it dissolve as illusions do?

!~~~~~~~!

In-focus has two distinct phases:

1. In-focus of energies which would otherwise be transmitted through the edge (subtle membrane) of the individual psyche. This means that energy which usually courses beyond the individual psyche is retracted into the psyche and conserved there. This the elementary part of the pratyahar sensual energy withdrawal discipline of yoga. It concerns the relationship between the psyche and the environment which surrounds it.

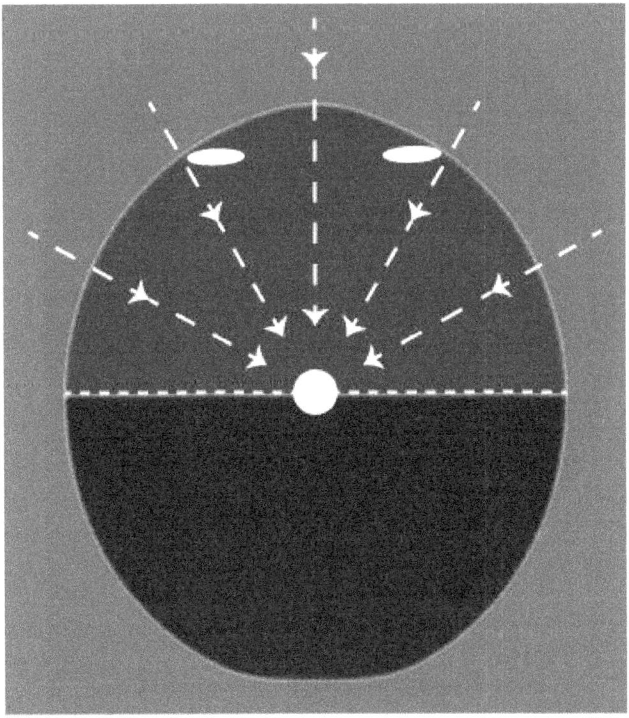

in-focus from objects outside the mind

2. In-focus of energies which would otherwise be transmitted through the edge (intense spiritual power limits) of the observing-self. This means that energy which usually manifest as an interest, is retracted into the observing-self and is conserved there. This is the advanced stage of the pratyahar sensual energy withdrawal discipline of yoga. It concerns the relationship between the observing-self and its personal adjuncts which are in the psyche. It is

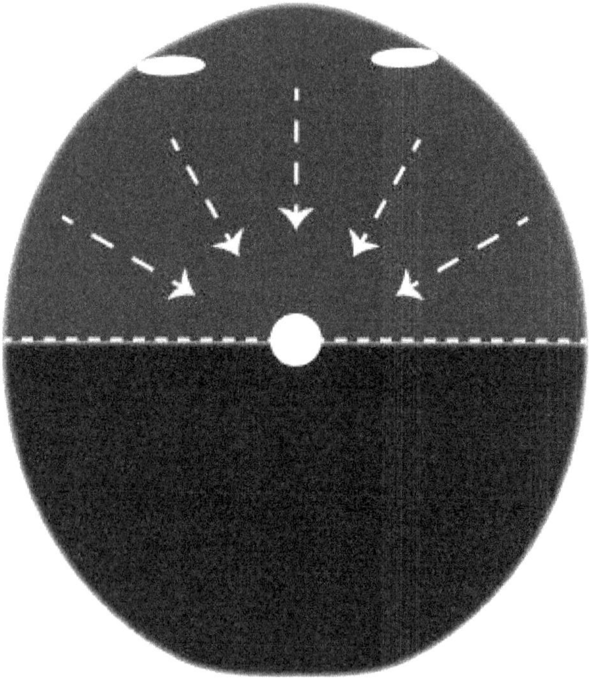

in-focus within the mind

not concerned with objects in the environment which surrounds the psyche.

So long as the person cannot sort the observing-self from the psychic adjuncts, that person should proceed with confidence doing an in-focus of his or her energies into the psyche. As soon as one is able to sort the observing-self and identify any of the adjuncts like the thought-making psychic mechanism, the kundalini life-force and the memory chambers, one should begin the practice of in-focus within the psyche with all interests being withdrawn into the observing self.

## *Non-focus*

Non-focus is rated as a yogic state when it is deliberately done as instructed in books like the Yoga Sutras. It is however a natural condition of mind which is assumed willingly or involuntarily. Non-focus occurs when the mind for one reason or the other, deliberately or undeliberately, is neither out-focused nor in-focused. It is unconcerned about anything. It does not want to be with thoughts or objects. Nor does it want to fold-in on the observing self. It is like a calm ocean. It is at a standstill.

non-focus within the mind

Patanjali levied an opinion about yoga. He said that it occurs under the condition of non-focus. He stated this:

योगश्चित्तवृत्तिनिरोधः ॥२॥

yogaḥcittavṛtti nirodhaḥ

*yogaḥ – the skill of yoga; cittavṛtti = citta – mento-emotional energy + vṛtti – vibrational mode; nirodhaḥ – cessation, restraint, non-operation.*

**The skill of yoga is demonstrated by the conscious non-operation of the vibrational modes of the mento-emotional energy. (Yoga Sutras 1.2)**

This is not an observer-less state. The observing-self is present but it lacks interest in anything in or outside the psyche. In the yoga process this state is achieved by a commanding willpower and also by other means like breath infusion and idea-less mental intent. It is not easy to master this non-focus. However, since the mind achieves this state from time to time, you may observe how it enters this condition as well as how it emerges from it.

When there is no activity in the mind, some persons experience that as boredom, which is undesirable. It can be experienced otherwise as a desirable state. This depends on the person's mental and emotional content. A question arises as to where the observing-self is located during a non-focus state. During a condition in which the self feels an attraction to thoughts or objects, the observing-self can be pin-pointed easily but when there is no compelling force in the mind, that self has little reference. Hence the difficulty in determining its location.

Through subtle observation, the observing-self can know where it is located just before the mind assumes the non-focus state. That last location can be considered to be its position. A man in a coma, after regaining consciousness may recall the last place he was aware of before losing objectivity. That for him would be the location.

Non-focus should be practiced in meditation. At first it will be momentary but if the student persists, the duration may increase. When there is an experience of boredom, the student should tolerate that for the time being but should not become absorbed in a feeling of disliking that condition. He should instead switch attention to sense the field of consciousness which is the non-focus condition.

How large is that field of consciousness?

How far out is it?

Some claim that it is infinite consciousness?

Is that your experience?

Some say that it is indistinct. Hence it is Absolute.

Is that your conclusion?

- Sit to meditate.
- Close eyelids.
- Notice the state of mind.

What is the condition?

Where is the observing-self in the mind space?

Has it invested interest in thoughts or objects?

Is it in a mind which has no focus, which is a diffused consciousness without interests?

## *Meditation Practice according to status of the mind*

Meditation procedure depends on the state of mind when you sit to meditate. It also depends on the meditation practice you learnt and is discovering and the direction that is taking from day to day. Some persons follow a stringent routine, or so they say. In reality, the mind drums up various states which confront the student and force changes in procedure. Let us say for example that my meditation should be that I have no thoughts or that I be detachedly focused on arising thoughts, or that I pay no attention to thoughts but instead focus on the rhythm of breathing. Can I say for sure that I do this during the entire meditation session? I can only say this if I have absolute control over my mental state, and that is impossible, because I do not have the supremacy.

It is only if the mind is conditioned to be a certain way habitually, then that state will be the default or regular condition of mind. Then I can rely on that say about 88% of the time when I sit to meditate. But even then there will be occasions when the mind regresses into undesirable behaviors leaving me to struggle to bring it the desired state.

The mind is like the weather which no man can absolutely control. When the climate is favorable we get things done quickly, otherwise we are force to suspend activities or work in an inefficient way.

These truths must be admitted by the meditator.

## *What to do when the mind is out-focused when you sit to meditate?*

The first action is mental. It is to realize that the mind is out-focused because if this is not realized, there will be no attempt to change the condition making it more suitable for meditation. Failure to realize that the mind is extrovert when it is at the beginning of a session, will result in the observing self's total absorption in the thoughts and desires composed by the mind as an interesting internal display. The mind will invoke memories and combine these with its currently stored ideas. It will imagine circumstances which will enthrall the observing-self.

Realizing that the mind is out-focused does not necessarily mean that this extrovert trend of the mind will cease. It may continue even after that is realized. There are many reasons for this continuation but the essential one is that the mind has some contents which has a power to enthrall the observing-self. Due to the way the observing-self observed some incidence(s) previously, that intent or careless viewing gives the memory of that concern the power to command the mental observer for a time. In meditation the observing-self will find itself to be hypnotized by the re-creation of one or more mental incidences.

As soon as you realize that the mind is out-focused, you need to remind yourself that your purpose is to meditate which is contrary to the out-focused condition which you observe. As soon as you remind yourself of this, you should take steps to reduce interest in whatever the mind is determined to be occupied with.

At this point you should reduce interest in the mind's creations. This is similar to reducing the current which flows through a light bulb. We may either operate a switch to dull the bulb completely. Or we may turn a dial which causes reduction in the current.

Which method should be used?

That depends on the command the meditator has over the mind. Those who meditated successful for some time, may abruptly cut off interest in the mind's images. These persons can then retract interest and keep the attention confined near to the observing-self. Then such an expert can do the desired meditation.

One who has no such command, should take steps to reduce interest in the creations of the mind. He should curtail the looking-tendency which sees the images projected by the mind within the mind. This could be a death struggle where the person finds that despite the desire to terminate this undesirable behavior, the mind continues and holds the interest of the observing-self against its will.

## *What to do when the mind is in-focused when you sit to meditate*

If the mind is in-focused when you sit to meditate, that is considered to be a gift of providence. This is exactly what is desired but it may also be problematic for those who are advanced.

For beginners an in-focused mind is success but for the advanced students, there would be an examination to see if the in-focus is supportive of the desired meditation practice.

What is in-focus?

What are the details?

In-focus means that the mind remains in the psyche with no urge to seek anything in the external environments.

This could mean the external physical environment, but it could, for advanced yogis, also mean no urge to seek anything in the external astral world.

What is the level of your practice?

Are you at the stage where no urge to seek anything in the physical environment is a big achievement?

Are you more advanced, where that achievement is elementary?

Suppose my meditation practice is that of a beginner. Then for me, any type of in-focus is a great achievement. To me that is everything. I am advanced. But what do I do next?

Where is the *me* in this consciousness which is in-focused?

Am I the entire psyche?

Am I a component in the psyche?

In-focus means that the mind lost interest in the external physical environment and/or the external astral (subtle) environment. It turned-in on itself.

In this state is the observing-self, the whole mind energy?

Is it, a part?

Obviously, if I am the observing-self, this implies that I am not the mind compartment even though I am a part of it as an observer within it. A man in a spacious tank, is neither the tank nor the air in the tank but he may be considered to be part of the tank if we choose to regard it in that way. He may be the only observer who can describe to us the surroundings within the tank.

Is there a focusing-center of consciousness in the mental energy?

Am I that focus?

There is energy which usually courses out of the mind into the external physical or astral environment. Now that this energy is reversed where does it go after it re-enters the mind.

Is it going into *me* as the observing self?

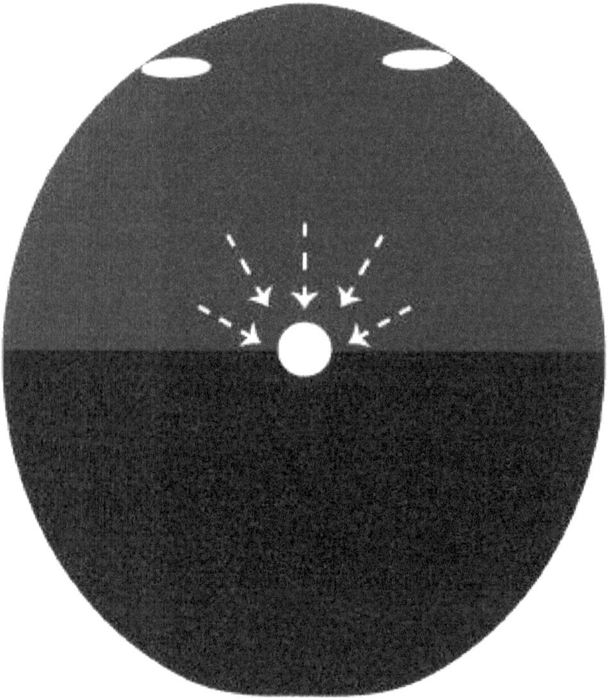

Is it going into random places within the mind environment?

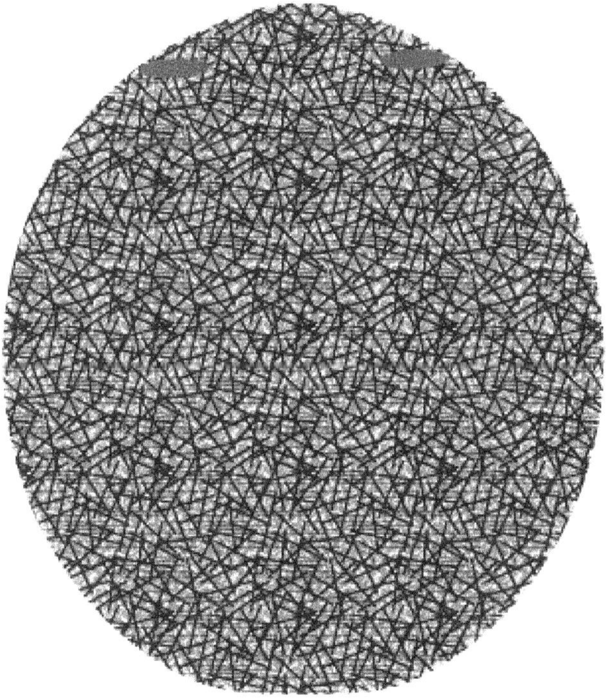

random energy

## ***What to do when the mind is not-focused when you sit to meditate***

If you sit to meditate and you find that the mind is in a not-focused state, where it is spaced-out or where it is laying as if it lacks interest in anything, then you should locate where you are in the mind. In this case, *'you'* means the observing-self in the psyche (self). You does not mean the whole self as a unit container of emotional and mental energies.

The convention is to rate the observing-self as the self or psyche, but for this practice, that identification should cease. For this, the observing-self is part of the psyche, part of the conventional self. Hence this observing-self is located somewhere in the psyche or self. It is not the entire self. It is not the whole composite but is only a significant part of it.

Even during a not-focused state, the observing-self is located somewhere in the psyche, somewhere in its mental and emotional energy.

Is such an experience of not-focus so abstract, that the observing-self cannot pinpoint or realize its location in reference to the other contents of the psyche?

The not-focused state varies from person to person, hence a general advisory about it would not be suitable to everyone. To advise you, a competent teacher would have to know your specific not-focused state.

Generally speaking, if the observing-self discovers itself in a not-focused state, it may simply relax and use the slight objectivity it has to realize where in the psyche it is located, as well as what else exists in the psyche and what potential there is for a relationship between itself and the other components of that state.

# Chapter 3

# Smelling Sense Focus

After establishing the value of a location for the observing-self, identifying what it is and knowing that it is a component in the psyche and not the whole psyche or conventional self, this meditation practice will shift to identifying the smelling sense faculty.

Each faculty is supported by an interest which is the common connection between the observer and that sense. We must consider this interest because it is the conduit between the observing-self and any sense faculty.

The smell faculty competes with other senses for the attention of the observing-self. In many animal species, this faculty is primal. It is dominant over the other senses. In a dog, for instance, the creature is seen to keep its nose near to the ground so that it can smell odors which indicate the presence of other creatures which it may attack, kill and eat. The dog uses its vision and hearing as well but the dominant one is this sense of smell.

In a cow we see the value of the sense of smell, where the animal may see a visually desirable object which appears to be edible but when the cow reaches within nose reach, the smelling compulsion dominates. If the fragrance is not agreeable it will neglect the object even if its eyes reports, that by the color, the object is appealing. In a cow's body, the sense of smell always supersedes the sense of sight.

In humans the sense of smell is not as predominant as it is in some other animals, but it does have a power over the psyche. On occasion, its opinions are considered final. They overrule every other sensual input.

In the diagram below please study where the olfactory sense is physically located, as well as where it is located in the subtle body. For that matter their location is the same vicinity; one being on the physical level; the other on the psychological plane. Our objective is to focus on the psychological level. In some applications the physical location interspaces the psychic one as in this case but that is not always true.

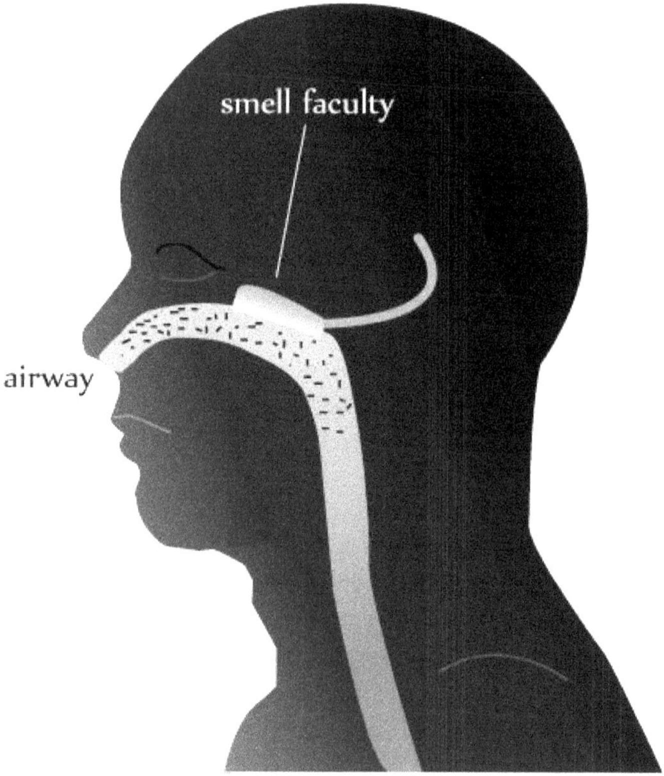


Each sense has a split configuration, for example two nostrils or two eyes. However in this meditative investigation, we wish to discover the sense faculty before it splits into two orifices. Our interest is the contact between the interest of the observing-self and the sense faculty.

- *Sit to meditate.*
- *Locate the observing-self.*

Those two instructions are the initiation of every meditation in this book. In a sense it is redundant to say that one should locate the observing-self because one is supposed to be that self. One should automatically know oneself and one's location.

However we know that because of the diffusion of awareness, the observing-self all but loses itself and becomes as if it was the entire psyche. Thus it is not silly to stress that one should self-observe the observing-self. Please therefore accept the suggestion. Do the following:

- *Sit to meditate.*
- *Locate the observing-self.*

As simple as this instruction sounds, it is not easy to achieve. It is not normal to identify this observing-self automatically when one introspects. The reality is that when one sits to meditate, the self does not at first discover itself. Rather it exists at that time as part of a circumstance, as if it merged into or melted into a circumstance. It has little or no interest in discerning itself. At first when one sits to meditate, there is a unity which is the psyche without any part of it being objective, but with every part being the occasion that is.

Hence the instruction is expanded to this:

- *Think of what you will do when you sit to meditate.*
- *Have a plan to disrupt the unity of the psyche, whereby as soon as you sit you discern and segregate the observing-self.*

- *Sit to meditate.*
- *Locate the observing-self.*

You must also have some way of bringing the observing-self into contrast with the rest of the psyche. Otherwise when you meditate the unity of the psyche will persist with minutes going by without the observing-self even knowing why the psyche sat to meditate. It will be unaware of its intention.

Even a proficient meditator finds that frequently when he (she) sits to meditate, some moments or minutes go by where there is no objectivity and hence no ability to cease the circumstance which the mind assumes. Think of deciding to go into a theatre but then finding that after you made the decision, you find yourself in that theater even though you made no effort to go there. Then when you discover yourself there, you discover yourself as a viewer, a person who sees the video or play which happens on the screen or stage. You discover yourself there but you have no memory of anything else. None of your objectives come to mind. You are there with no sense of direction except whatever is shown in the video or acted by the actors in the skit.

How long will this transpire?

When will you become objective?

Let us begin this instruction again. Previously we did not reach the objective. We became enthralled when we internalized in the mind. The likelihood was that regardless of the objective before closing the mind to the external physical environment, once the closure occurred, mainly by closing the eyelids, we found that it was a circumstance.

Here is the instruction again:

- *Think of what you will do when you sit to meditate.*

- *Have a plan to disrupt the unity of the psyche, whereby as soon as you sit you can discern and segregate the observing-self.*
- *Sit to meditate.*
- *Be aware of what transpires within the mind space.*
- *Locate the observing-self.*
- *Notice how it is occupied or entertained in whatever circumstance the mind pursues, either as thinking afresh, imagining, remembering, mixing ideas or not conceiving.*

Then there arises the question of what to do next. As soon as there is this objectivity whereby one realized that as the observing self, one is in contrast to all else in the mind, one may still not know how to proceed. One may have no awareness of the objective. Even if the observer had an objective, he (she) may not locate it and may be at a loss of what to do in the mind. This is because the objective package of energy may be separated from the observer such that the observer cannot be self-situated. Have you ever found yourself lacking in a certain memory, either a recent or remote one?

What happened to that package of information?

Why could you not access it?

Why did you have to wait minutes, hours, days, weeks or years thereafter, until the mind made it available again?

Let us make another attempt to complete this meditation:

- *Think of what you will do when you sit to meditate.*
- *Have a plan to disrupt the unity of the psyche, whereby as soon as sit you discern and segregate the observing-self.*

- *Sit to meditate.*
- *Be aware of what transpires within the mind space.*
- *Locate the observing-self.*
- *Notice how it is occupied or entertained in whatever circumstance the mind pursues, either as thinking afresh, imagining, remembering, mixing ideas or not conceiving.*
- *Self-instruct the observing-self to cease interest in the mind's circumstance, to turn its concerns upon itself, to forgo all other occupations of mental and/or emotional constructions. At this point the psyche which was one unity will appear to be two constituents, one being the observing-self which instructs itself and the other being whatever else is there in the psyche which surrounds that observer.*
- *Focus that observing-self more upon itself. Make it retract more of its interest which was invested in whatever else the rest of the psyche was involved in.*

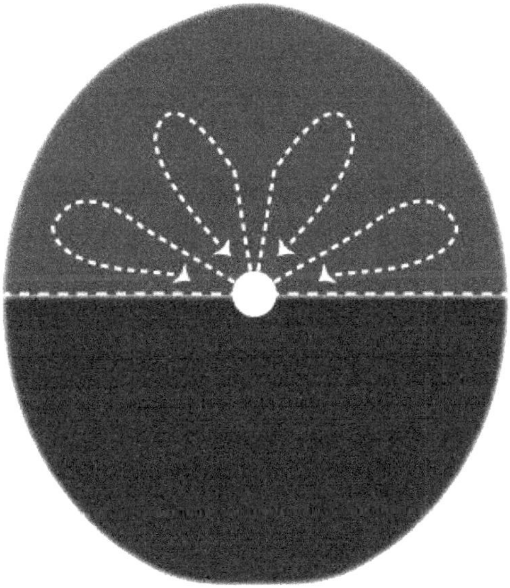

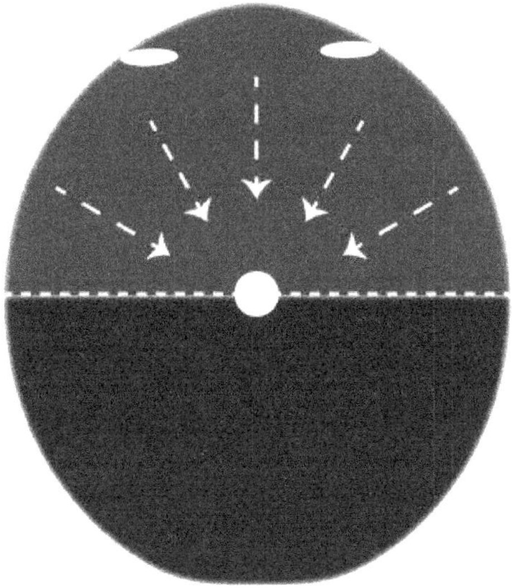

in-focus within the mind

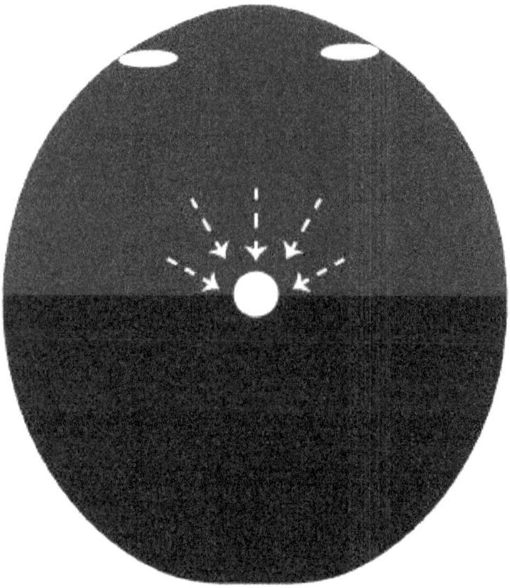

- *Pull that self together as itself. Resist any urge to be interested in whatever the mind does within itself. Be callous and disinterested into whatever the mind has as its occupation. Repeatedly resist. Turn away from feelings and mental activities. Focus interest fully on the observer.*

- *Maintain this self-interest behavior, this introspection on the observing self. Retract even the tiniest interest that pursues other activities within the mind space.*

- *Check for the position of that observing-self. Where is it in terms of the mind space? Is it in the middle of the space? Is it in the back of the space? Is it in the front of the space? Is it the observer and the blank mind? Is it the observer and a thought-occupied mind? Is it the observer with attractive or repulsive memories?*

We made some progress in the procedure but this chapter concerns discovery of the smelling sense. Once the observing-self completes the preliminary meditation of locating its position and keeping that self in isolation with its interest in itself, then the observer should direct his (her) attention to the subtle smell faculty.

Let us again do this practice and go a step or two further:

- *Think of what you will do when you sit to meditate.*
- *Have a plan to disrupt the unity of the psyche, whereby as soon as you sit you can discern and segregate the observing-self.*
- *Sit to meditate.*
- *Be aware of what transpires within the mind space.*
- *Locate the observing-self.*
- *Notice how it is occupied or entertained in whatever circumstance the mind pursues, either as thinking afresh, imagining, remembering, mixing ideas or not conceiving.*
- *Self-instruct the observing-self to cease interest in the mind's circumstance, to turn its concerns upon itself, to forgo all other occupations in the mental and emotional constructions. At this point the psyche which was one unity will appear to be two constituents; one being the observing-self which instructs itself; the other being whatever else is there in the psyche which surrounds that observer.*

- *Focus that observing-self upon itself. Make it retract more of its interest which is discovered and was invested into whatever else the rest of the psyche was involved in.*

- *Pull that self together as itself. Resist any urge to be interested in whatever the mind is doing within itself. Be callous and disinterested into whatever the mind has as its occupation. Repeatedly resist and turn away from the mental activities. Focus the interest of the observer upon the observer only.*

- *Keep this self-interest behavior, this introspection towards the observing self, focused on that self. Retract any little interest that pursues other activities within the mind space.*

- *Check for the position of that observing self. Where is it in terms of the mind space? Is it in the middle? Is it in the back? Is it in the front? Is it just the observer and the blank mind? Is it the observer and the thought-occupied mind? Is it the observer and attractive or repulsive memories?*

- *Intensify that observing-self upon itself. Focus it on itself.*

- *Gather the interest-energy of that observing self.*

- *Invest that interest-energy on that observing self, so as to intensify and concentrate that observer.*

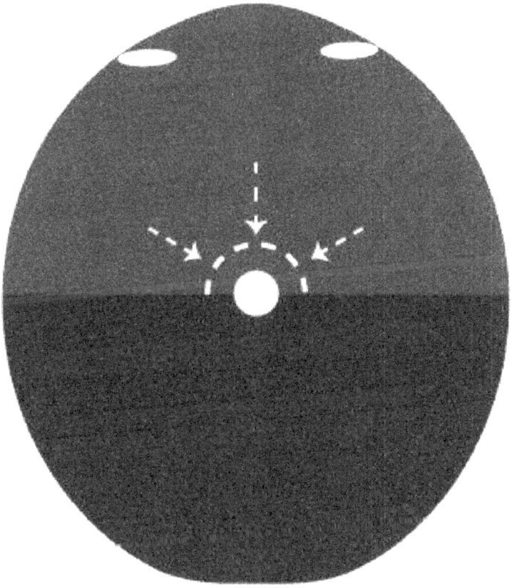

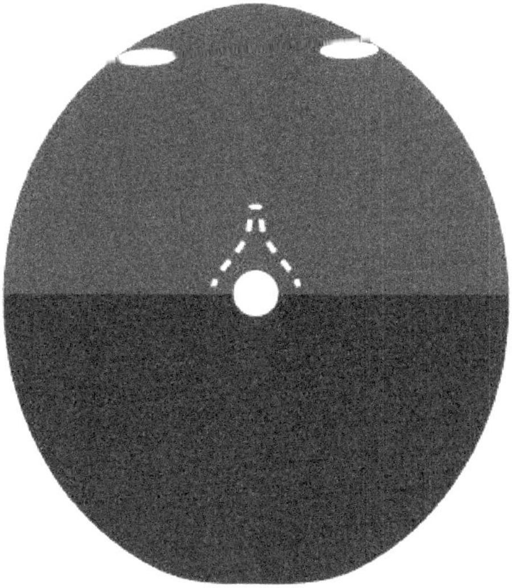

- *Direct that interest-energy into the space where the smell faculty is located in the subtle body as in this diagram:*

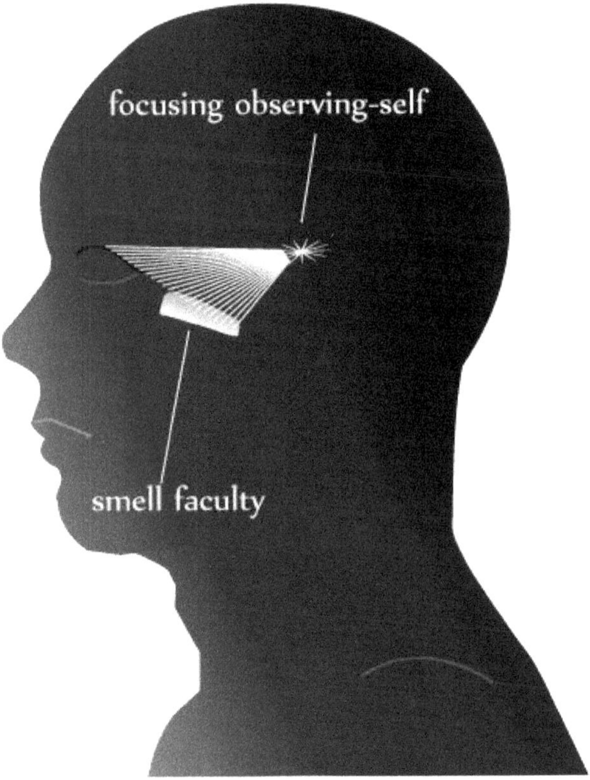


Please bear with this practice even though some phases of it will be without rewards, without light in the mind, without pleasure or happiness. Admittedly, this practice is abstract. The sense faculties are designed to give excitement, either desired feelings or repulsive reactionary responses. Their coding is that If there is no attraction, they either enter into a neutral mode or direct the interest-energy to another sense faculty which has excitation. The mind in turn interprets a lack of excitement as boredom, as cause of disinterest or disappointment. This produces an impetus to pursue any hint of excitement which is given by any other sense. If a hint is discovered the interest-energy abandons the boring sense and invests itself in excitement. Please understand this. Be patient with this process but do not take sides with the boredom-mood or the disappointment-feeling which is emitted by the sense which finds no exciting attractions.

Once you locate the observing-self and realize it as being resistant to thoughts and ideas, direct its interest to this space. Keep its interest there as if you are silently waiting for something to happen. Never mind the boredom or lack of excitement. Merely remain with the interest being directed to that subtle space. Ignore any feelings of disappointment. Leave aside any urge to shift to a more exciting sense faculty.

You should locate that subtle place exactly as shown in the diagram or very close to that location. Once you locate it, focus on it. In this you need to keep three objectives. The primary one is the observing-self. The next in importance is the smell faculty location. The least is being aware of the rest of the mind contents so that the observer does not come under the spell of the imagination.

If for any reason the observer is hypnotized again, he (she) will lose focus on the smell faculty. Then an effort must be made to reconnect. Keep your interest at the faculty even if there is no odor, even if it is devoid of smells. A lack of odor is interpreted by the mind as a lack of interest or as a withdrawal of interest with intentions to find something of value, to find another sensual occurrence through the same or some other sense faculty. The mind has an innate dislike for a lack of sensual absorption. Except when it is in a stupor or is drowsy, it routinely turns away from sensual blankness.

However for this practice, we need to suspend this mental attitude. Stay in the blank space where the sense faculty is located, with that faculty hanging there empty with no subtle particles of odor for analysis.

Repeatedly do this meditation, day after day, preferably twice per day for a time, until you slide into the procedure when you sit to meditate. When you feel proficient, when the routine seems natural, when the mind automatically does this, include this procedure:

- *As soon as the interest is invested in the smell sense faculty location, as soon as it is rested there, with the observing-self not being distracted by mental interplay, lift the interest and the smell faculty location.*
- *Repeatedly make the effort to lift it as in this diagram*

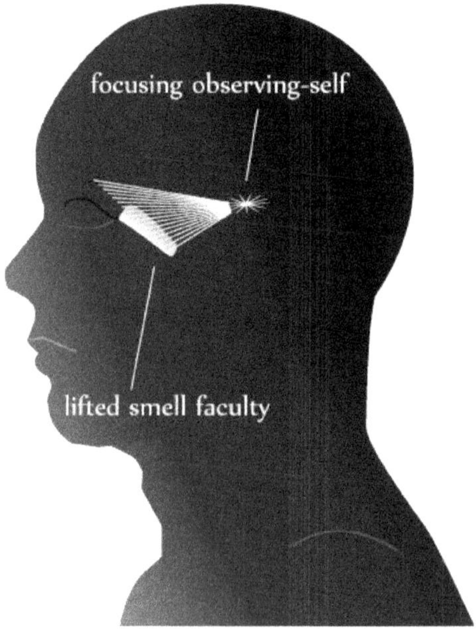

- *When the lifting action is natural even if there is resistance to it, lift it a little more until you feel that the smell faculty drops to its default position and the lifting action remains upward without it. Hold this action as it is.*

- *The lifting action is a psychic one. However, the smell faculty will yield partially, but not fully, to this action. As you lift higher and higher, a downward-pulling force will cause the smell faculty to release itself from the interest energy. The smell faculty will fall to its default position. Your interest-energy will be left upwards hanging in mental space.*

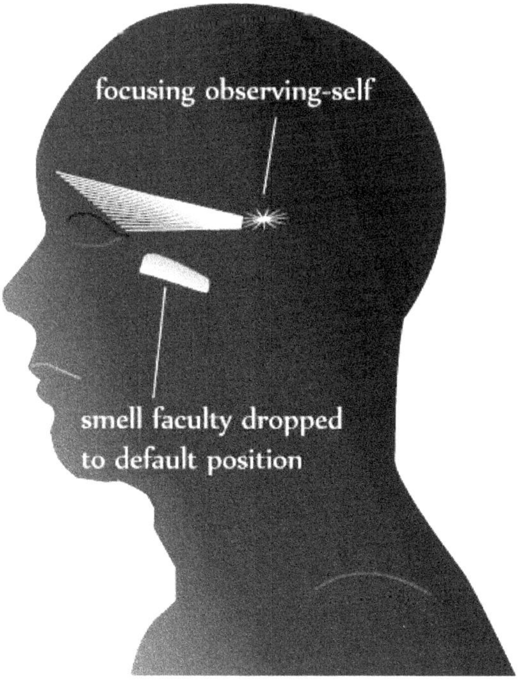

- *When the lifting action is left hanging in mental space, make no effort to reconnect it with the smell faculty which dropped to its default location. Be attentive to the interest-energy only. Hold it where it is, where the sense faculty separated from it. Notice that the interest-energy feels lighter as if it lost weight due to the release of the smell faculty. It should feel much lighter and easier to direct.*
- *Slowly lift the interest-energy further. Notice that it has a tongue-like insertion which seems to separate from it as it rises above eye level. Notice as well that further back into the head the interest-energy and this tongue-like insertion are connected at a place where it seems that the tongue-like insertion begins.*

Examine this diagram:

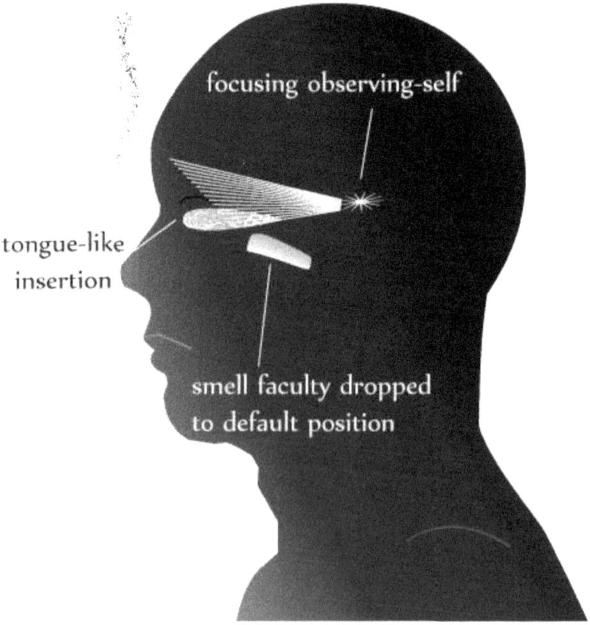

Repeatedly do this meditation until you reach the procedure which causes you to observe the interest-energy and the tongue-like insertion connection-area. In meditation, hold your attention on this circumstance for as long as you can, even for five or fifteen minutes.

Please review details of this meditation:

- *Think of what you will do when you sit to meditate.*
- *Have a plan to disrupt the unity of the psyche, whereby as soon as you sit you can discern and segregate the observing-self.*
- *Sit to meditate.*
- *Be aware of what transpires within the mind space.*
- *Locate the observing-self.*
- *Notice how it is occupied or entertained in whatever circumstance the mind pursues, either as thinking afresh, imagining, remembering, mixing ideas or not conceiving.*
- *Instruct the observing-self to cease interest in the mind's circumstance, to turn its concerns upon itself, to forgo all other occupations in the mental and emotional constructions. At this point the psyche which was one unity will appear to be two constituents; one being the observing-self which instructs itself; the other being whatever else is there in the psyche which surrounds that observer.*
- *Focus that observing-self upon itself. Make it retract more of its interest which is discovered and was invested into whatever else the rest of the psyche was involved in.*

- *Pull that self together as itself. Resist any urge to be interested in whatever the mind is doing within itself. Be callous and disinterested into whatever the mind has as its occupation. Repeatedly resist and turn away from the mental activities. Focus the interest of the observer upon the observer only.*

- *Keep this self-interest behavior, this introspection towards the observing self, focused on that self. Retract any little interest that pursues other activities within the mind space.*

- *Check for the position of that observing self. Where is it in terms of the mind space? Is it in the middle? Is it in the back? Is it in the front? Is it just the observer and the blank mind? Is it the observer and the thought-occupied mind? Is it the observer and attractive or repulsive memories?*

- *Intensify that observing-self upon itself. Focus it on itself.*

- *Gather the interest-energy of that observing self.*

- *Invest that interest-energy on that observing self, so as to intensify and concentrate that observer.*

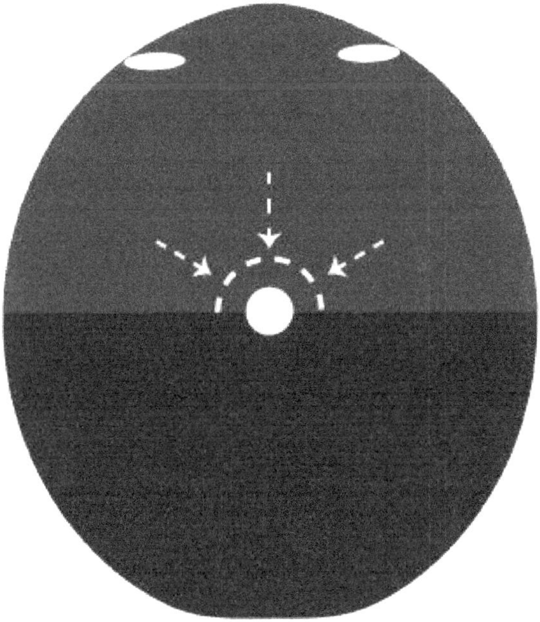

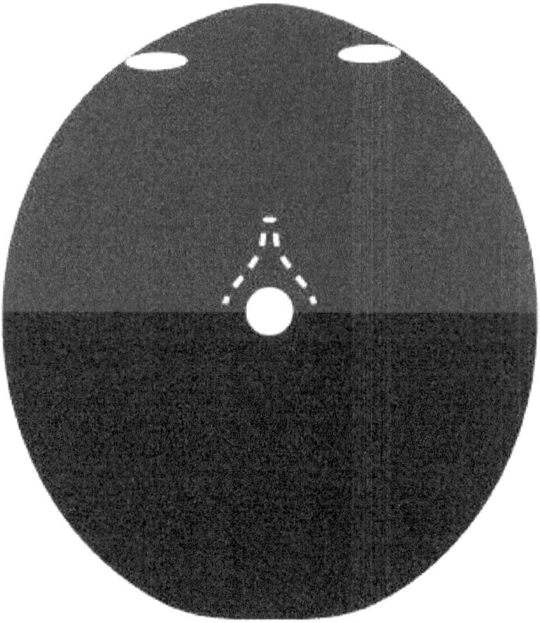

- *Direct that interest-energy into the space where the smell faculty is located in the subtle body as in the diagram below:*

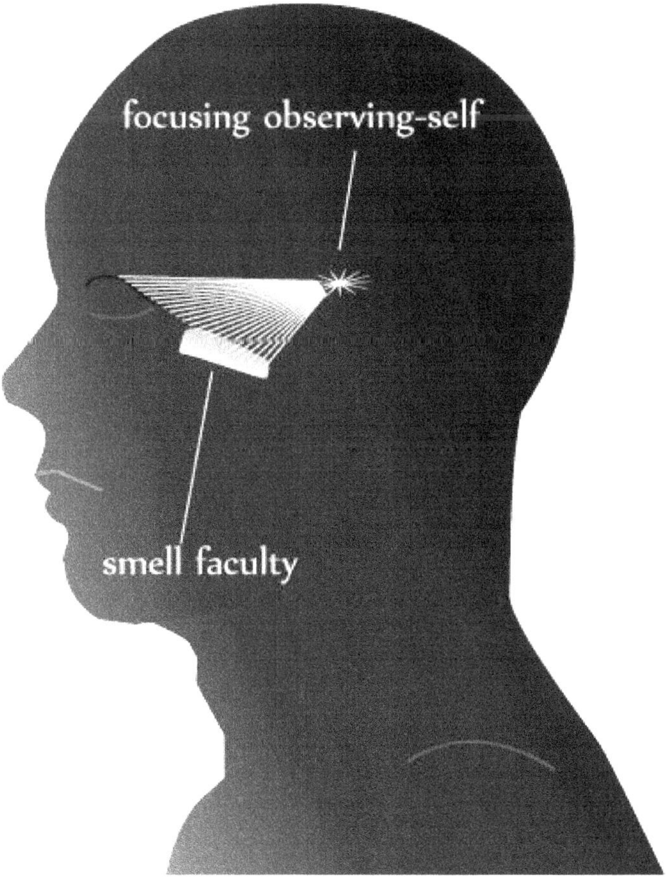


- *As soon as the interest is invested in the smell sense faculty location, as soon as it is rested there, with the observing-self not being distracted by mental interplay, lift the interest and the smell faculty location.*

- *Repeatedly make the effort to lift it up as in this diagram*

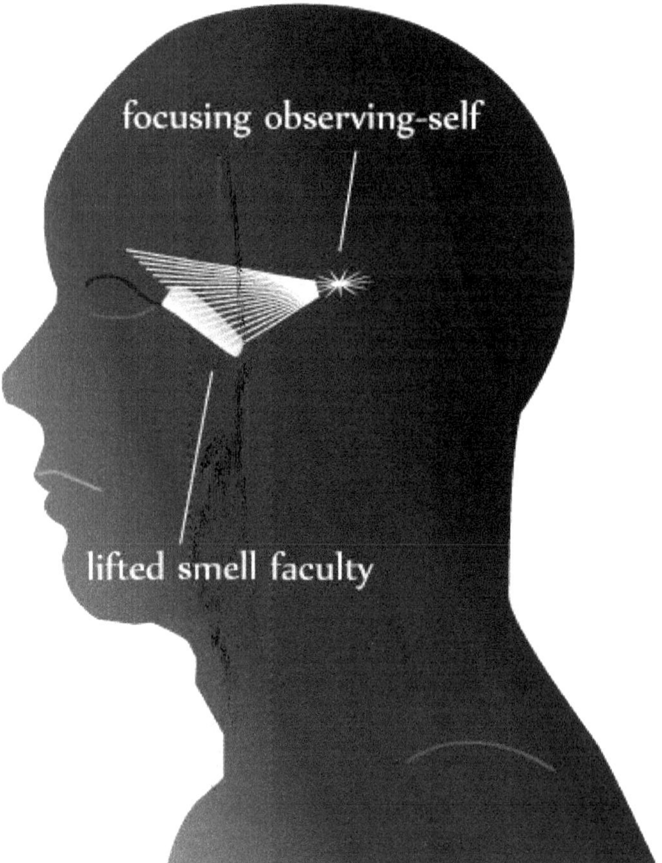


- *When the lifting action is natural even if there is resistance to it, lift it a little more until you feel that the smell faculty drops to its default position and the lifting action remains upward without it. Hold this action as it is.*

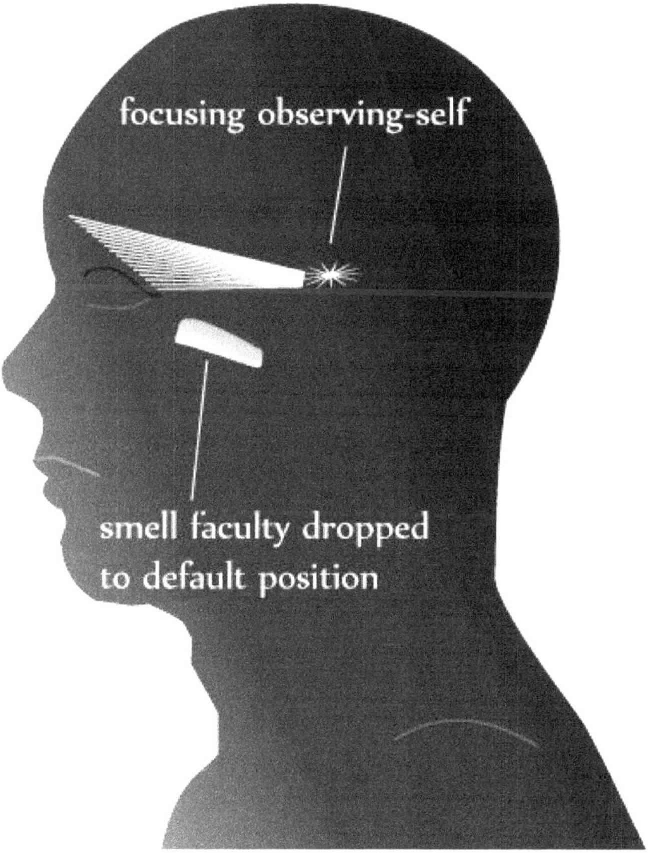


- *The lifting action is a psychic one. However, the smell faculty will yield partially, but not fully, to this action. As you lift higher and higher, a downward-pulling force will cause the smell faculty to release itself from the interest energy. The smell faculty will fall to its default position. Your interest-energy will be left upwards hanging in mental space.*
- *When the lifting action is left hanging in mental space, make no effort to reconnect it with the*

*smell faculty which dropped to its default location. Be attentive to the interest-energy only. Hold it where it is, where the sense faculty separated from it. Notice that the interested energy feels lighter as if it lost weight due to the release of the smell faculty. It should feel much lighter and easier to direct.*

- *Slowly lift it further. Notice that it has a tongue-like insertion which seems to separate from it as it rises above eye level. Notice as well that further back into the head the interest-energy and this tongue-like insertion are connected at a place where it seems that the tongue-like insertion begins.*

Examine this diagram:

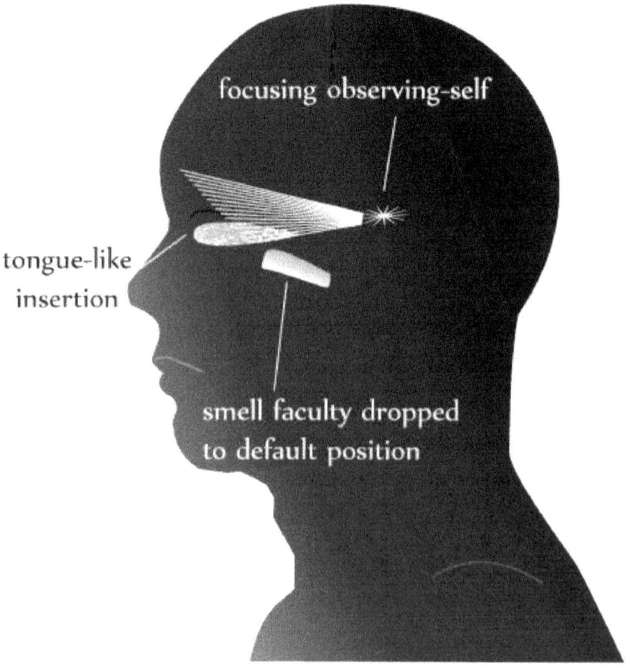

Please repeat this meditation until you are proficient in it, until the mind ceases to divert to something else, or where even if the mind initially is engaged in some other focus, it ceases that soon after you sit to meditate. Of its own accord or with very little prodding, the mind should execute the procedure outlined. It should reach the stage where the interest is raised above eye level and is experienced with the tongue-like insertion.

Once you gain proficiency, consider that the tongue-like insertion is not our interest in this meditation. We are concerned with the interest-energy which is above it. Anchor your attention into that energy. Abandon concerns for the tongue-like protrusion. Focus into that interest-energy as shown in this diagram, where it seems that the tongue-like protrusion drops out of focus or enters a darkness and is no longer detected.

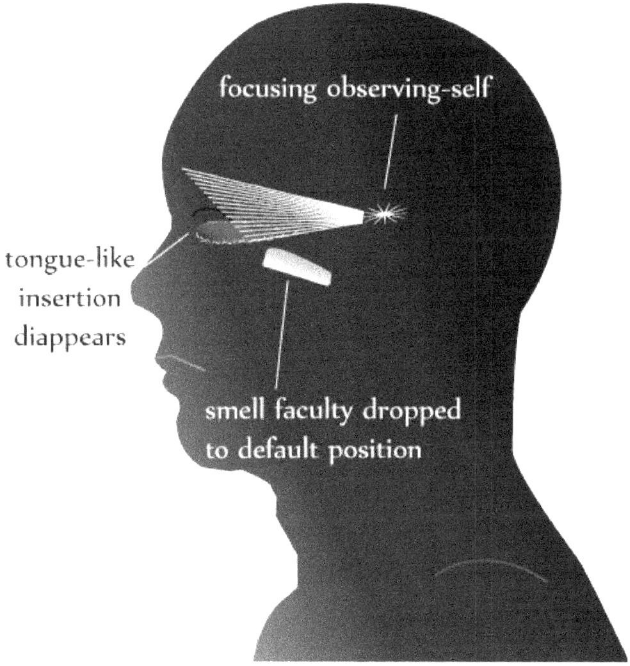

- Gain proficiency in this focus on the interest-energy with the tongue-like protrusion being present but of no mental register. Slowly pull back this interest-energy as if to shrink it backwards, as if to cause it to withdraw itself towards the observing-self which is in the existential center of the mental space. Keep retracting and reducing the interest energy.

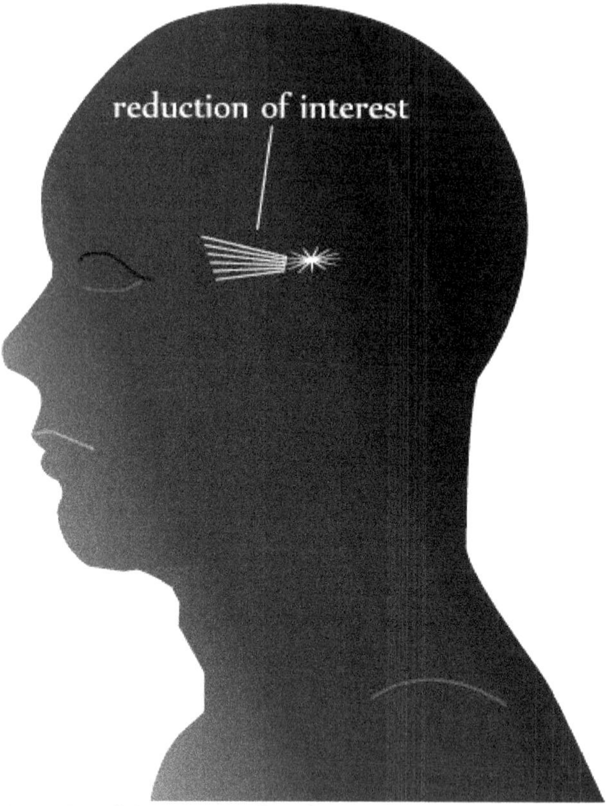


Practice this repeatedly. Then proceed with this action:

- Direct the shrunk interest-energy downward towards the smell faculty. Do this carefully so as not to touch the tongue-like protrusion energy. If the interest-energy touches that energy it will again fuse into that energy. For this meditation, that connection is undesirable. If it happens accidentally or because of not controlling the attraction between the interest-energy and the tongue-like protrusion force, begin again with the shrunk interest energy. Carefully go downwards so as to avoid contact with the tongue-like protrusion, then go across

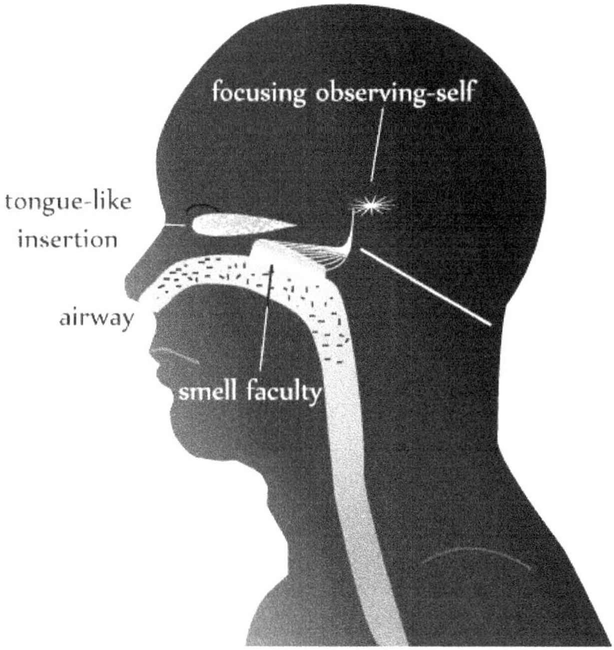


to the smell faculty. Practice this again and again until you find that the interest-energy is trained to avoid the tongue-like protrusion force.

- Link the interest-energy to the smell faculty. Keep it linked there in a relaxed meditation.

> Seek no odors. Be satisfied during the meditation to be experiencing the neutral stage of the smell faculty. Do the meditation until you become proficient.

Repeatedly achieve this meditation. The lack of a response-smell should be tolerated. This is an abstract meditation, where only the interest-energy should be invested with no presence of an odor to excite it.

## *Odorless ~ Odorladen Air*

For this practice our interest is the odorless air. We investigate the smell sense faculty not the smell or odor which it detects. The presence of an odor causes changes in the sense faculty which robs the person of the ability to distinguish between the faculty and the odor.

Consider pure water in a transparent jug. Consider if red dye is added. As soon as the red dye is included, it will dominate anything which tries to perceive the water, whereby the red color will be a distraction which will pull the interest-inquiry of the observer. Hence only pure water should be used even though that is quite abstract in comparison to the colored type.

Neutral investigation has the disadvantage of a lack of excitement but that is the very reason why it is valuable. Be confident that it will yield clarity.

The smell faculty has all independence when it does not detect an odor. It loses that as soon as an odor is present because then its mode of neutrality is lost. As soon as an odor is detected it is forced to process, identify, rate, reject or crave the odor. This automatic operation, once started, causes it to spin while making the calculation as to the value of the odor. The report of this value causes the mind to make a decision regarding if the entire psyche should endeavor to procure more of the odor. The mind might decide that the psyche should distant itself, or merely tolerate the odor. This switching action of the mind, where it procures information and then makes decision, disrupts clarity. Please therefore agree that for this meditative investigation the persistent desire to sense excitedly should be suspended.

# Chapter 4

# Tasting Sense Focus

The tasting sense is the subject of this chapter. Here again we will regard the neutral blank state without variation. The physical organ involved is the tongue. During the practice, we will curl the tongue and push it towards its root into the soft palate. With the tongue inserted into the soft palate focus the interest-energy below that area, at the root of the tongue.

Taste sensors reside in the tongue in various places but our concern is the root where the interest-energy is invested before it is diverts to the various tasting cells which detect sweet, salt, savory or neutral tasting objects.

For this practice, the proficiency developed in previous chapters will be used. Unless it is forcibly pulled down below the eye level in the body, the interest-energy usually stays high-up in the subtle head.

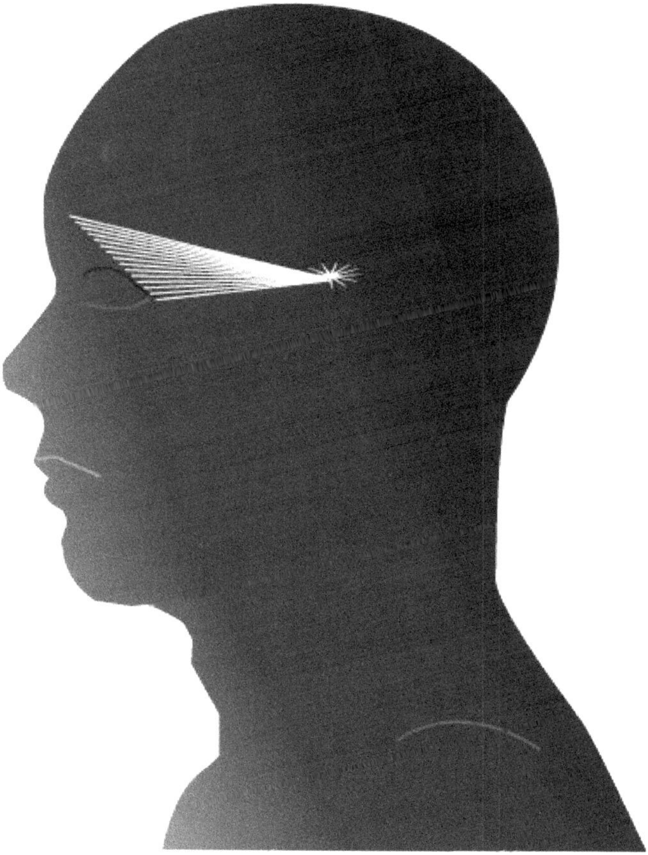

Usually the eye level is the default focus level of the interest energy. It is prone to being unified with the visual sense in a human form and with the smell sense in many of the quadrupeds. The interest energy, due to its visual sense orientation, is reluctant to become unified with the tasting sense except when there is a compelling tasty treat, or a repulsive flavor, detected by the tongue. This means that to get the interest-energy to lodge into the root of the tongue when that organ is in its neutral state will be a challenge.

At first we must double check to be sure that when sitting to meditate, the mind assumes a state which is supportive of self-focus on the observing-self.

- *Sit to meditate.*
- *Note the condition of mind.*
- *Figure how long it took for you to be objective to the mind's theatrics.*
- *Was it immediately after you sat?*
- *Did it take some moments or minutes when you realized that you were enthralled by images and ideas?*
- *Did you struggle to cease the mind's thoughts?*

The subject of why the mind does not draw a blank when that is desired, is an old discussion among yogis. We are in a long list of ascetics who were confronted with this undesirable but natural way of the mind, which obstructs deep insight during meditation.

The subjects of imagination may be related to recent occurrences, remote memories or fresh mental constructions which are novel even to the mind. Why does the mind hash over these impressions?

Why does it subject the observing-self to such influences?

Why can the observing-self not command the mind to cease this activity?

Each idea in the mind has a different attacking power within it. One idea can be easily banished. Another may persist even after the observer exerts willpower to terminate it.

What are the parameters which determine the power of an idea over the observing-self?

Can the observer carefully regulate his (her) interest in future occurrences such that memories do not have a hypnotic influence?

- *Sit to meditate.*
- *Note the condition of mind.*
- *Figure how long it took for you to be objective to the mind's theatrics.*
- *Show some interest in whatever the mind illustrated so that you get some idea of the power of that particular imagination.*
- *Pull the observing-self out of the display in the mind.*
- *Let that observer recede to the back of the head, moving backwards little by little.*
- *Observe how the mind's hypnotic influence deceases as you move away from the frontal area.*
- *Remain at one place in the back of the subtle head, with the frontal part of the subtle head being devoid of ideas or images, being blank.*
- *Slowly come forward to the default location of the observing-self, the central place within the awareness in the subtle head.*
- *Become stabilized at this default location with the observing-self being resistant to imaginations of the mind.*
- *The tendency to look forward is felt at this place. Ignore that urge. Close the interest in anything which is in the frontal part. Keep the interest-energy near to the observing-self. Do*

*not allow it to reach forward through the subtle head.*

Even though we suggest that one not allow the interest-energy to be pulled through the subtle head, still this will happen. There will be a struggle to stop this. You will fail on occasion, such that no matter what you do, no matter how much you exert, still your interest will be pulled into the theatrics of the mind.

This is because you do not have absolute control over the mind. During some meditations, yes, you will find that the mind is cooperative and everything goes according to plan. During other meditations you will find that it is a death struggle with the observing-self being ignored by the mind?

It is left to you to solve the puzzle of why you have control on one occasion and then lose in another meditation session. Keep practicing regardless because that is the only way to increase the degree of control.

Let us begin the practice again, except that we will go a step or two further:

- *Sit to meditate.*
- *Note the condition of mind.*
- *Withdraw your interest in the mind's theatrics. Be objective. Move away from the mind's illustrations.*
- *While at a distance from the ideas, show some interest in whatever the mind illustrates so that you can gage the power of that particular imagination. What was the source of it? Was it a memory? Was it a fresh mental construction? Was it a recent sensual contact?*
- *Abandon interest in the mind's display.*
- *Let the observer recede to the back of the head, moving backwards little by little. Be sure to*

*note that this is not spontaneous. There is resistance to this. The observer seems as if it is glued to the existential center of the mind, looking forward through the mind.*

- *Observe how the mind's hypnotic influence deceases as you move away from the frontal area. Yet, also observe that the observing-self is a bit uncertain of itself as it moves backwards. This suggests that the observer has confidence in the mind's theatrics and relies on being very close to the mental space where the theatrics occur.*

- *Remain at one place in the back of the subtle head, with the frontal part of the subtle head being devoid of ideas or images, being blank. If at this place, the observing-self feels isolated and devoid of sensual treats, then encourage the self to persist. Let the self be confident that sooner or later it will return to the theatrical displays.*

- *Slowly come forward to the default location of the observing-self, the central place within the awareness. If you find that the mind attempts to lure the observing-self into viewing ideas or images, recede to the back of the head again. Shut down interest in the front of the subtle head as you do so. Close off the vision tendency which attempts to see forward through the subtle head. There are no eye lids as in physical perception but there is a closing of the visual interest faculty. That will seem to be a closing curtain before the observing-self, keeping it from seeing what is before it in the mind.*

- *Become stabilized at the default location with the observing-self being resistant to imaginations of the mind. To assist the observing-self, it should keep its interest-energy very close to it, while being satisfied with being without sensual illustrations.*
- *The tendency to look forward is felt at this place. Ignore that urge. Close the interest in anything which is in the frontal part. Keep the interest-energy near to the observing-self. Do not allow the interest-energy to reach forward through the subtle head.*

The observing-self should stay put at its default position with its interest confined near to it and not being expressed to anything. The observer should turn the interest upon itself and remain as if frozen in time, as still as it can be, without expression of interest beyond itself.

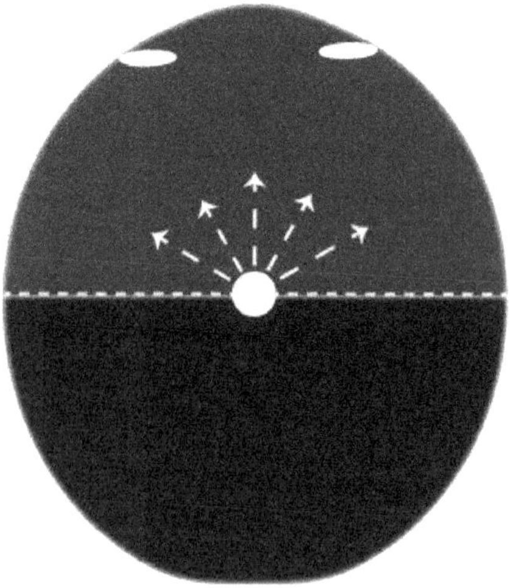

attention searches the mind for ideas

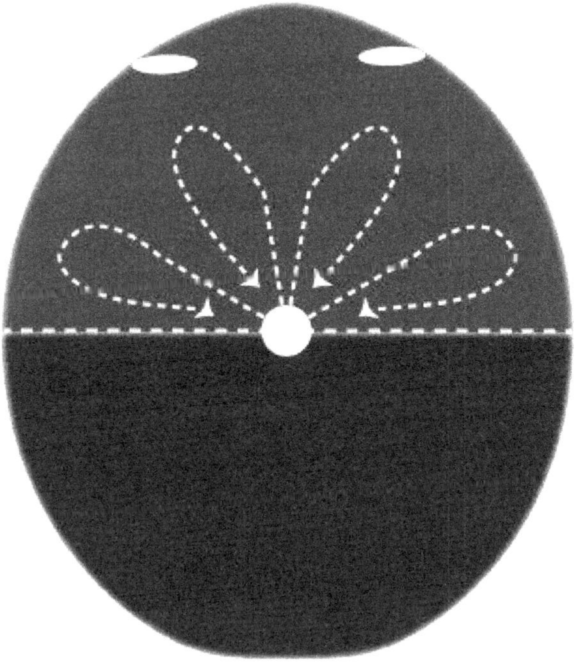

attention leaves the observing-self
and loops back to that self

The controlled application of the observer's interest is done when the interest-energy is freed from being influenced by the thought-image display and the emotional interplay of energies which are in the psyche. This is an achievement but it is an unnatural condition which must be earned through earnest meditation.

What is natural is not always in the interest of the observing-self which means that it must earn the changes which are required. Everything beneficial is not gifted by nature. Some desirable features must be endeavored for.

Once the interest-energy is confined to the observing-self, that observer can direct this energy instead of being induced to accept whatever attracts the interest. The convention is for the observing-self to follow the lead of the interest energy, which in turns follows the lead of the thought-image display, which in turn follows the lead of sensual inputs which are freshly acquired or which are reenacted by the acquisition of memories. This is a convenient convention but it is not useful in this practice.

- *Enter into meditation as described previously. Then with the interest-energy confined and obedient to the observing-self, direct that interest downward in a curve so that it reaches the root of the tongue. When it reaches the root, you will find that the location is abstract. It can hardly be pin-pointed. At that time curl the tongue up and push it back to the soft palate. Focus on this action of the tongue. Localize the focus on the place where the tongue pushes into the soft palate. Keep the focus there.*

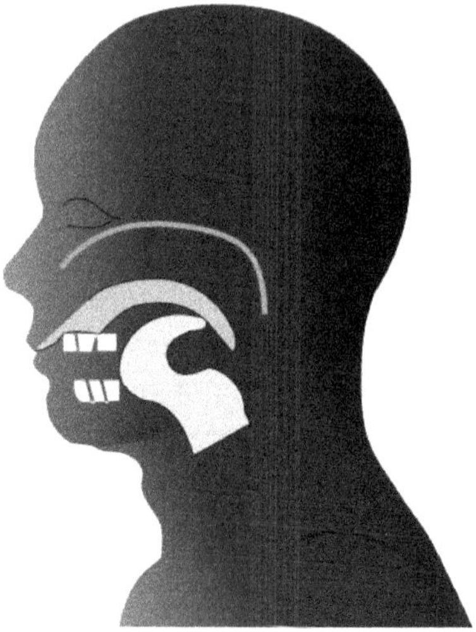

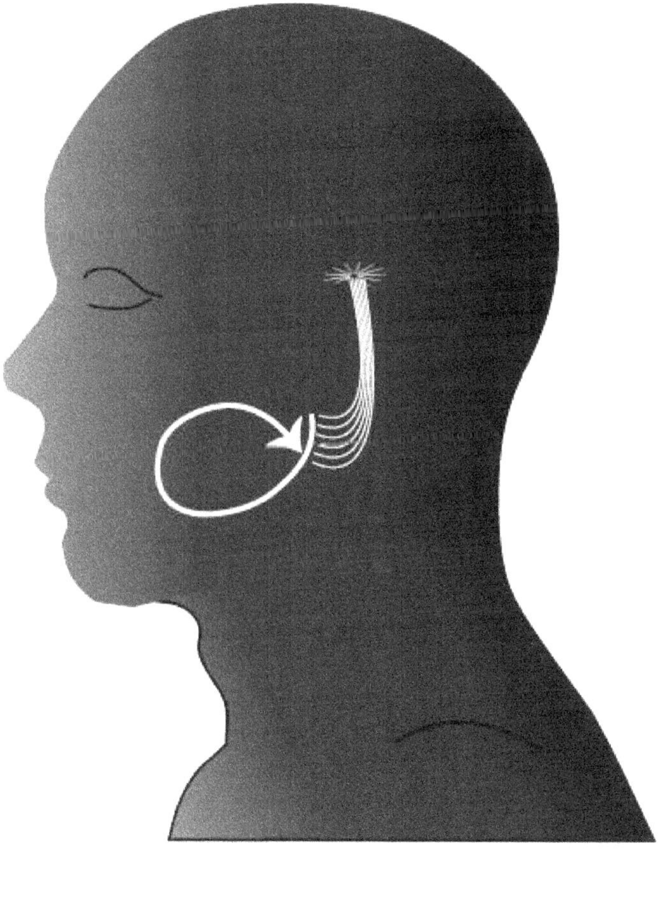

- *Recheck to be sure that the interest-energy is contained and remains invested in the soft palate where the tongue is inserted. Be sure that the interest did not wonder to another focus. If it has, you should retrieve it to the observing-self. After it becomes stable, you should again direct it downward in a curved*

*way so that it reaches where the tongue pushes into the soft palate. Hold the interest-energy there. This may require increased focus. This may seem unnatural because usually the interest goes in a forward direction in the subtle head. Its convention is to make contact with the thought-image display location of the mind. There it usually proceeds to connect into the vision energy.*

- *With the interest-energy being held at the place where the tongue pushes into the soft palate, notice a mineral taste there which consist diversified micro-flavors. These flavors cannot be identified as salty, sweet, savory or bland. These are micro assets of flavors which are present in the saliva of the body. This is a chemical composition of many types of taste.*
- *As the tongue is pushed into the soft palate and the interest-energy is invested there, one will notice that the tongue stiffens. The chin will shift upwards. At this point do not allow the physical chin to move. Instead only allow the subtle chin to do so while the physical one remains positioned as before.*
- *To distinguish between the physical and subtle chins, first hold the physical chin in place. Then let the shifting force affect the idea of the physical chin. This idea of that chin is actually the subtle chin which is composed of subtle ideation energy.*
- *When the interest in the pressure point where the tongue pushes into the soft palate is intensified, there will be an upward flow of energy. One will realize it as a loop flowing*

*down through the back of the trunk and up through the chest in the front.*

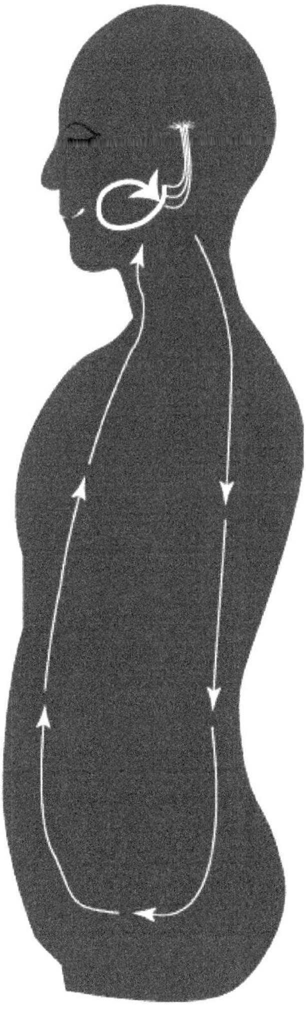

This flow of energy is a continuous loop of taste molecules. These flow because of a biological and psychic electric current which is produced by the attraction between the taste faculty and the reproduction functions. In the psyche of those who do asana postures and pranayama breath infusion, these energies circulate in a much more efficient way than in others.

By remaining aware of this continuous loop of taste molecules, one will notice that it consists of globules, bead-like droplets which keep turning as the loop ventures the route

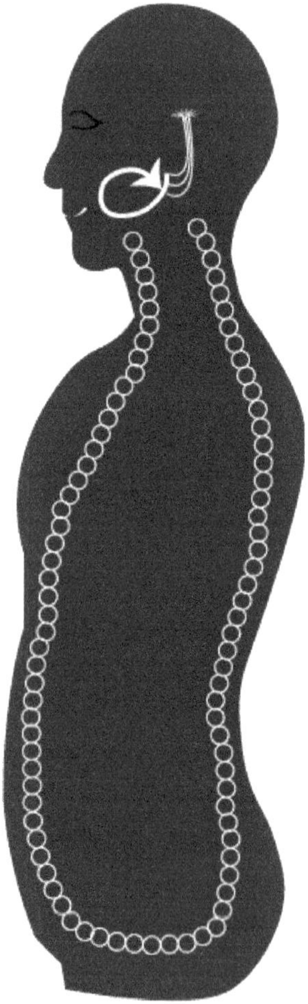

By repeated focus on the taste faculty as described, there will be a shift where the interest moves into the chest area. This will be a shift from the taste faculty to the packaging area of whatever was eaten.

When the yogi is shifted to the chest area, it will seem as if that part of the body is an absorbent pad which is laden with flavors. The yogi should stay in the chest area in many meditations, so as to get insight into the relationship between tasting, eating and digesting.

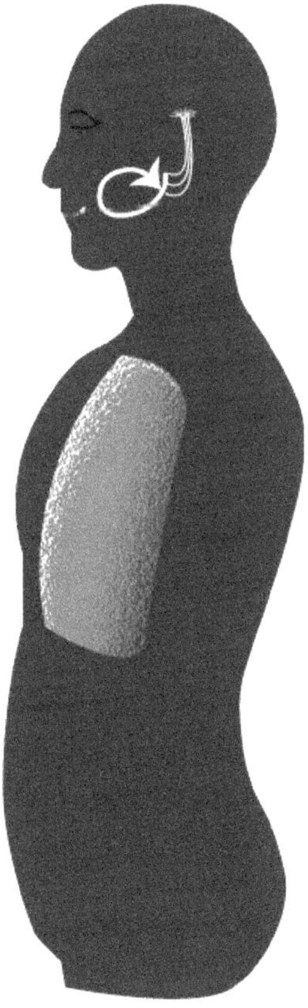

# Chapter 5

# Sight Sense Focus

For this practice, great care should be taken to control the relationship between the observing-self and the sight faculty. This faculty exacts great dependence from the observing-self; hence the need to curb the relationship between the two. If the observer cannot be freed from its reliance, he (she) will be unable to separate the interest from the sense faculties, which will result in a total failure to control its interest.

The reliance on sight perception of material objects and sight perception of abstract or astral objects is a need to contend with. However a yogi should not be scared to forego sensual access during the meditation period. Think of it! If you meditate for thirty minutes or for two hours even in each day of twenty-four hours, that is not the majority of your time. Can you spare yourself the visual perceptions for thirty minutes or two hours?

It is crucial that we understand the value and promise of shutting down the physical and lower astral perceptions. Curtailing these is the way to develop higher astral perception and even causal apprehension of super-subtle realities.

- Sit to Meditate.
- Be sure to check the condition of the mind. Bring it to order where the interest-energy retracts to the observer and loses interest in the mental display.

- Once the interest-energy is retracted and is by the side of the observing-self or is folded into that self, gather that energy to be sure that part of it is not involved in the mental displays.
- Check to see if the mind demands the attention of the observer. Is the mind quiet and lacking mental activity or emotional interplay? Or is it active and compelling?
- Bring the mind to order where it does not demand attention. If you find that you cannot achieve this, postpone the meditation on the sense faculty. Instead study the condition of the mind. Take note of its contents. Realize why this specific content deprives you of the right of achieving absolute blankness of mind.

Did you invest more attention than you should have in a particular sensual experience? Was your investment involuntary where you did not have a choice because the sensual information charmed you and disabled your purpose?

Was it music?

Was it sexual pleasure?

Was it a violent physical or video scene?

Was it gossip?

Was it strong attachment?

Dissect the mental display. Realize why it acquired the power to compel you to be under its influence.

Make a plan not to be enticed by this type of incidence. Realize that until its power diminishes you must bear with this obstruction.

It is important to dissect compelling ideas and images within the mind. One should know what is irresistible both in the physical existence and in the imagination realm of the mind. Imagination has power to control the observing-self whereby the observer thinks that it constructs thoughts and ideas when in fact it is subjected to these theatrics.

Honesty is necessary, where one can admit that one does not have the required control, and that one is controlled for the most part by the scenery in the mind. Gaining this insight does not immediately grant the observer control but it does produce the desire to strive for independence. Over time if one practices enough meditation, one will find that little by little one gains, step by step, more and more mind control. It will be incremental however.

- *Sit to meditate.*
- *Pull back all interest-energy into the observing-self.*
- *Do this sufficiently and powerfully so that there is a pulse in the pull, a throb.*
- *Pull in a semicircular manner.*

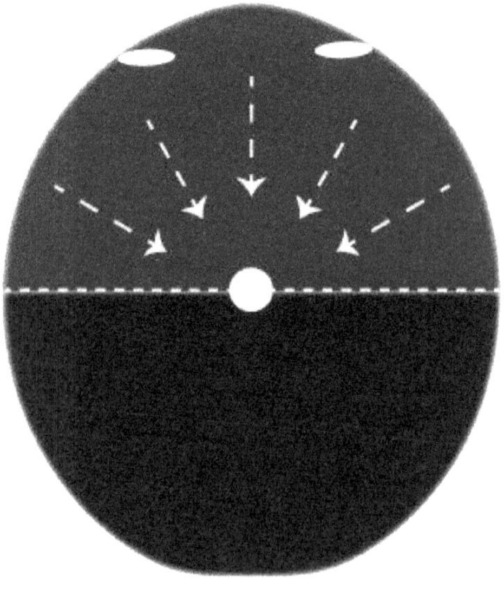

- *Pull in three directions.*

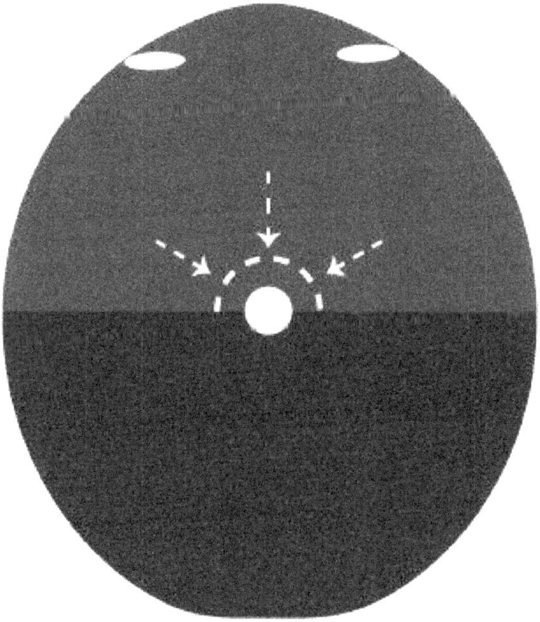

- *Keep the line of sight low at the top or slightly below the nose bridge:*

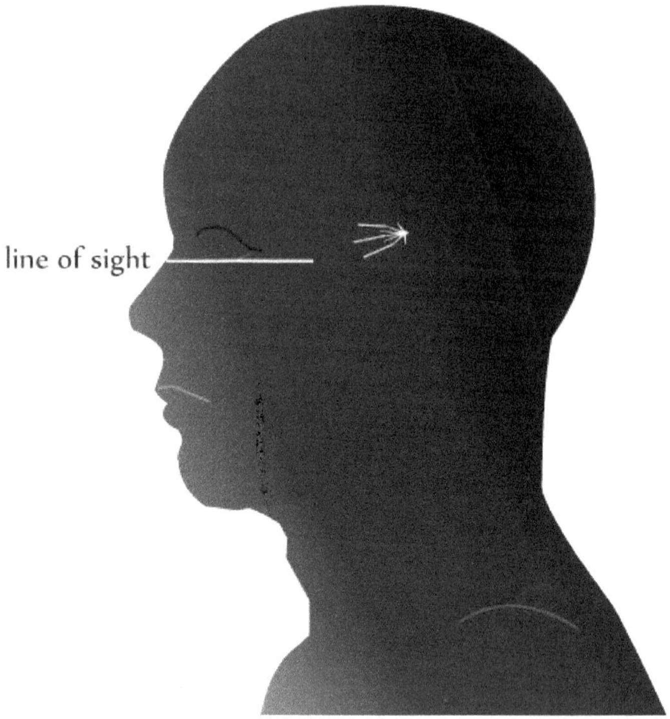

- *Release interest-energy in a fine stream smack center but simultaneously hold the interest-energy to the self in every other direction. The smack center release should be laser-like.*

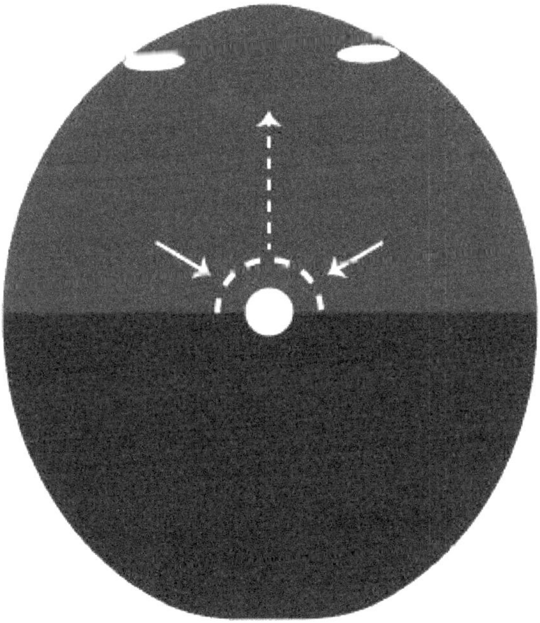

- *Keep the smack center focus pointed away from the observing-self as all other interest-energy is focus into the observer.*

- *Notice that the smack center focus disappears and is absorbed into a blank or dark grey space.*

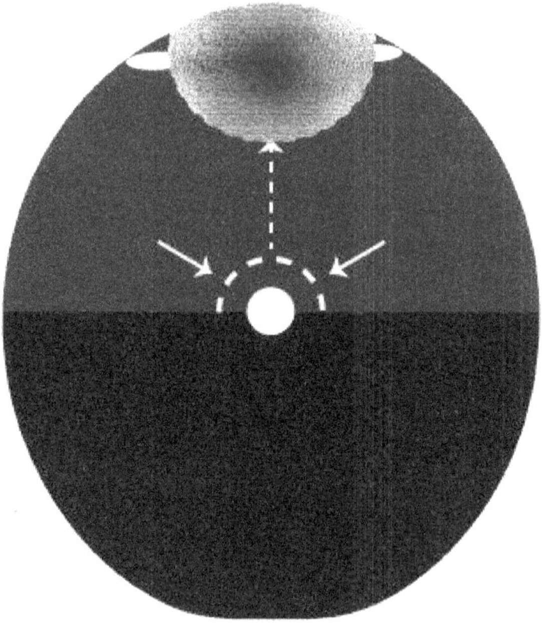

- *Continue this laser focus smack center but pull all energy in from each side.*

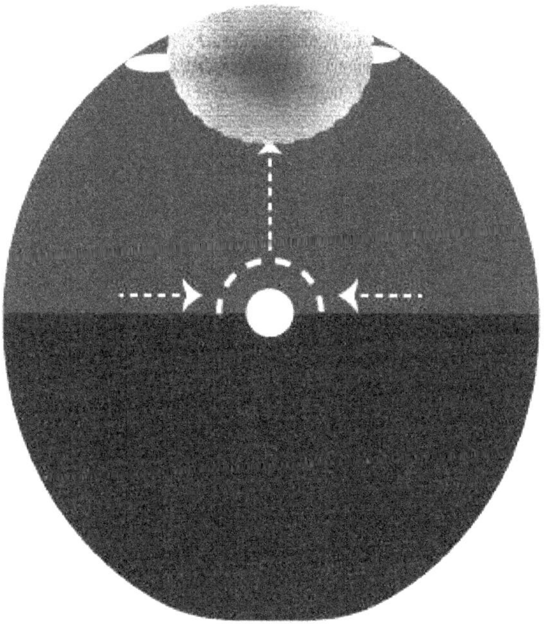

- *Continue the laser-like expression which disappears as it travels forward.*

- *Pull energy from the back of subtle head into the laser-like interest energy.*

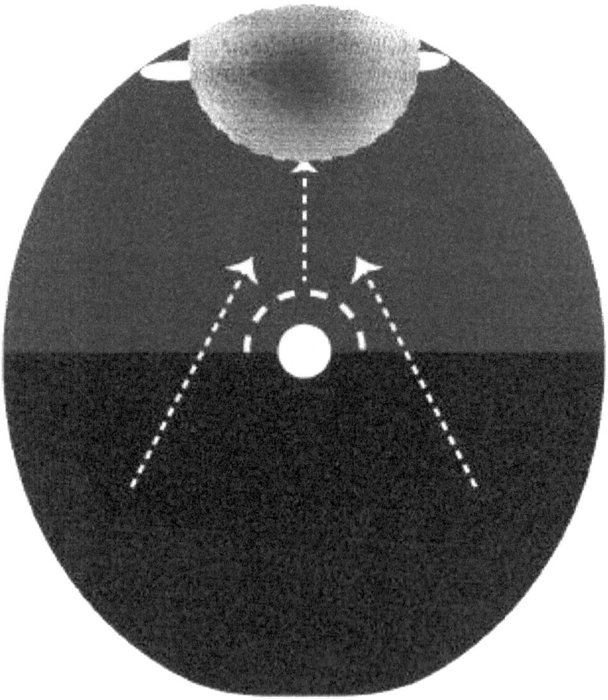

- *Pull energy from directly behind the observing-self while transmitting interest forward in a laser-like beam.*

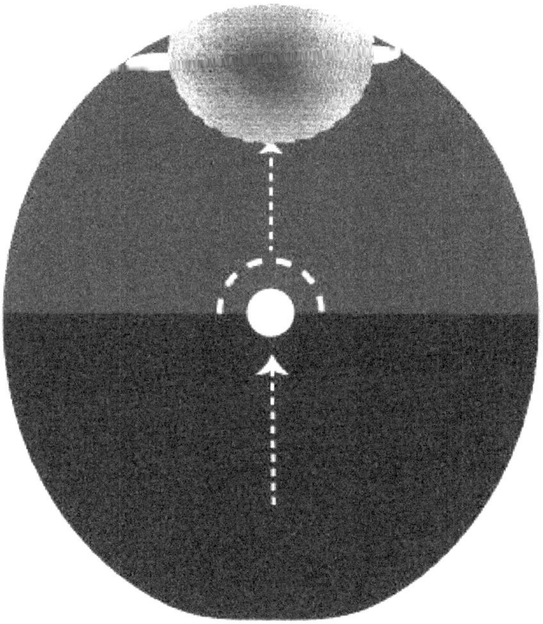

- *Release the interest laser focus to the front. Focus only on pulling energy from the back.*

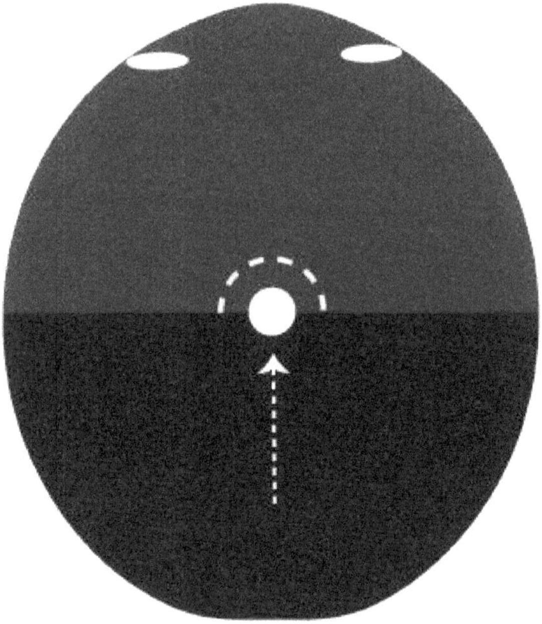

- *Regain the laser-like focus to the front. Release pulling energy from the back.*

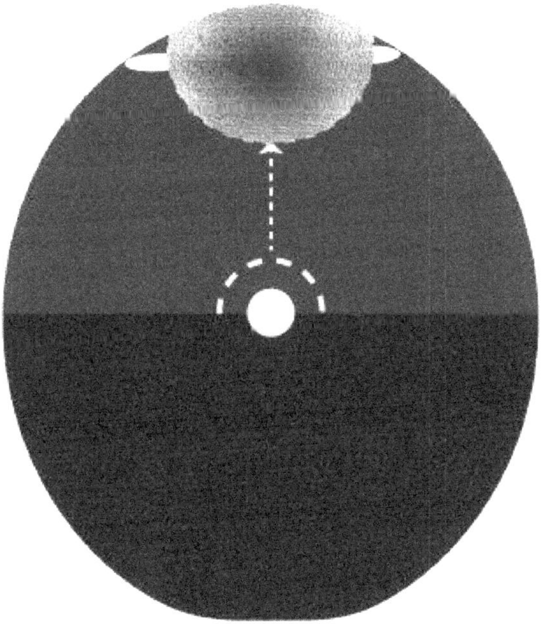

- *Release the laser-like front focus. Draw energy from the back.*

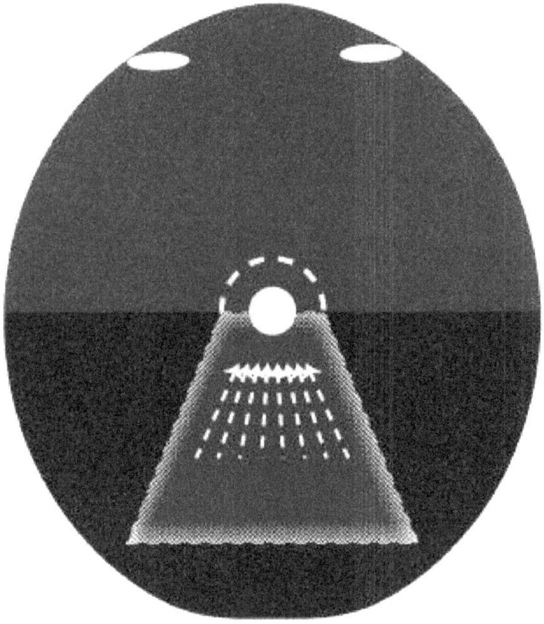

- *In a slanted pull, draw energy from the bottom back.*

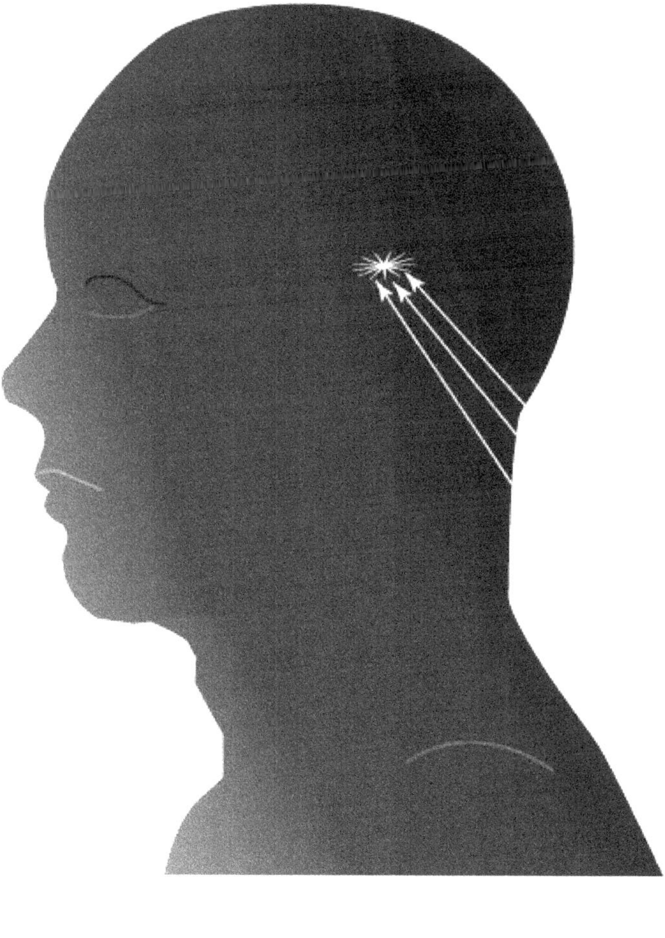

- *Switch the attention to the central throat. Link energy from that place to above the observing self.*

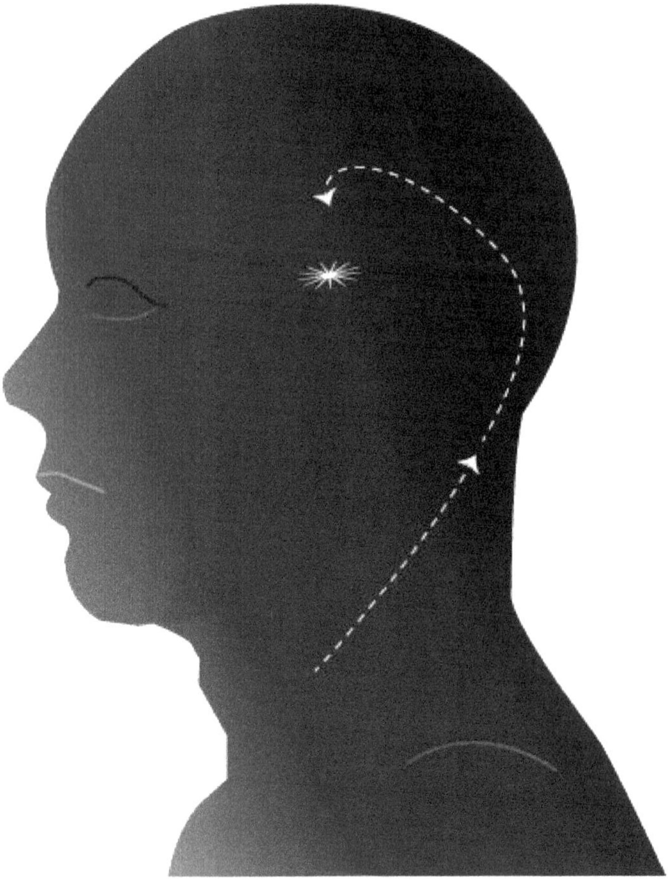

- *Sense an astral globule to the left front of the observing-self. This globule is invisible but is detected in meditation when the observing-self is not harassed by thoughts and ideas.*

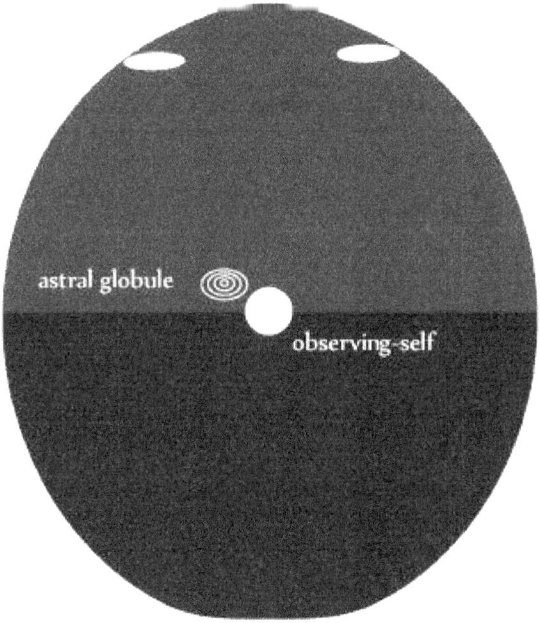


- *Remain with awareness of the observing-self and the astral globule. Do so until both fizz out. If you did not become aware of the globule continue this procedure by being aware of the observing-self only. When it fizzes out, you should hear a screeching noise. Soon after*

*there will be an all-surrounding noise. This is the naad sound resonance in the head of the subtle body. Do not regard it as a nuisance sound, but do not focus on the sound either.*

- *Look forward through the space in the subtle head. Feel the interest-energy fused into the vision energy in one laser-like beam. If the beam drifts up or down, to the left or to the right hold it steady center. Do not permit it to project beyond the forehead of the subtle body. It should stay within the subtle head. It should have no interest in seeing beyond it.*

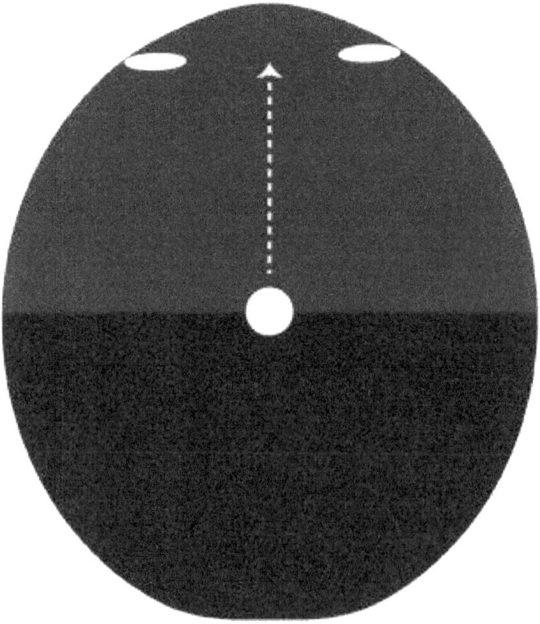

# Chapter 6

# Touch Sense Focus

The skin of the body is the primary touch receptor. When we investigate internally we find that the skin is relevant and has a major part to play. In the subtle body there is a subtle membrane which seals in whatever the psyche comprises, just as there is a physical skin which seals in the organs, tissues, bones and fluids of the physical system.

In sexual intercourse a human may discover that the skin of the male genital and the lining of the female one are both charged with sensations, which we call feelings. This is based on the proliferation of the touch sensation. Rudimentary life forms like amoeba are totally reliant on their membrane for information about what happens in the environment. This is the value of the touch faculty.

Because it is so diversified and extensive, the touch sensation is perhaps the most difficult to realize. Still, the effort should be made to understand how it operates. So much of what we do is based on its influence. According to biology the hand of the physical body is comparatively the most sensitive in terms of touch but the hand is excelled by the membranes and cells of the genitals.

The hairs, micro hairs and internal cilia, are the sensors which trigger responses which are interpreted by the skin and inner linings of the body. In the subtle body these hairs form an aura or strands of subtle energy of varying colors.

So far in this book, we established the observing-self and its interest energy. These will be used as applications for the rest of the practice.

- *Sit to meditate.*
- *Observe the condition of mind.*
- *Do whatever is necessary to increase objectivity.*
- *As the observer gather your interest close to you.*
- *Retract that interest from all other concerns.*
- *Be disinterested in whatever the mind imagines as thoughts or ideas.*
- *Focus on the membrane of the subtle body.*

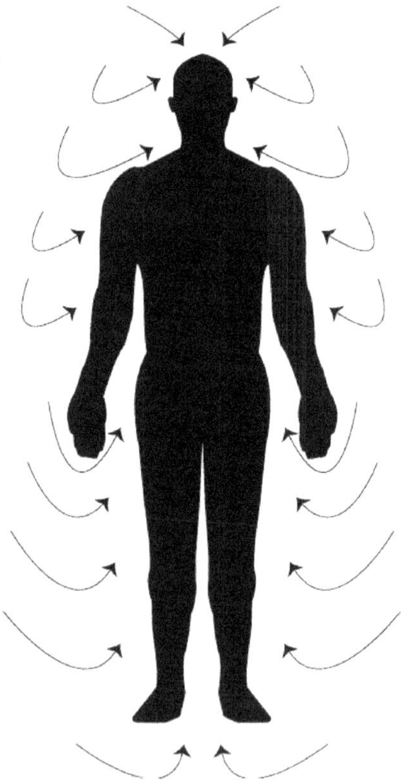

In this practice the skin of the physical system is useful because the membrane of the subtle body is interspaced in the physical one.

- *Focus on atmospheric energy pressing in on the subtle membrane which forms the border between your psyche and the environment around it.*
- *Keep the focus on the subtle membrane.*
- *Experience a constant trickle of energy inwards from the membrane.*
- *This energy will be coming away from the membrane going inwards and then disappearing.*

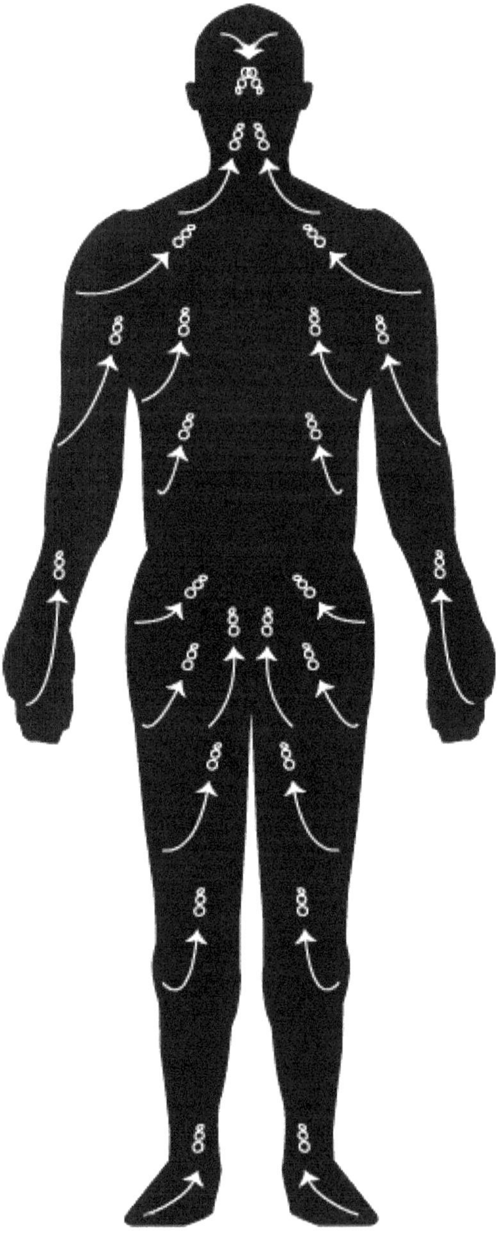

- *As you focus on this inward-moving trickle of energy, you should hear a screeching sound. Recognize it but leave it aside.*
- *Focus on the inward-moving energy which is usually interpreted as feelings.*
- *Make an effort to turn out those touch sensations.*
- *Direct them to leave through the subtle membrane.*

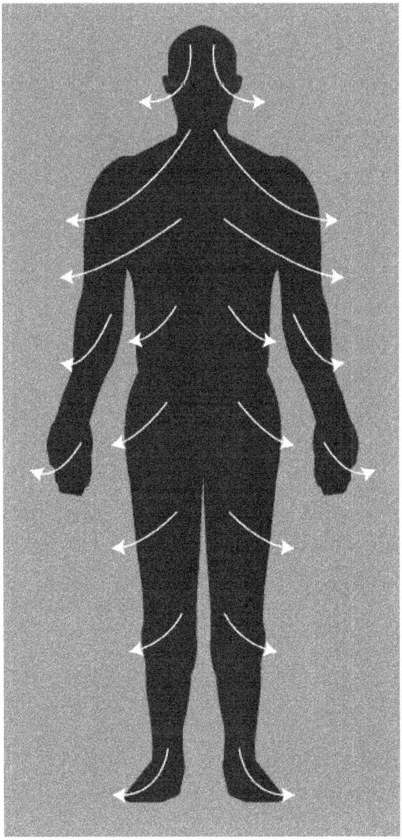

- *Reverse the process, where the sensations of feeling come into the body from the external environment.*

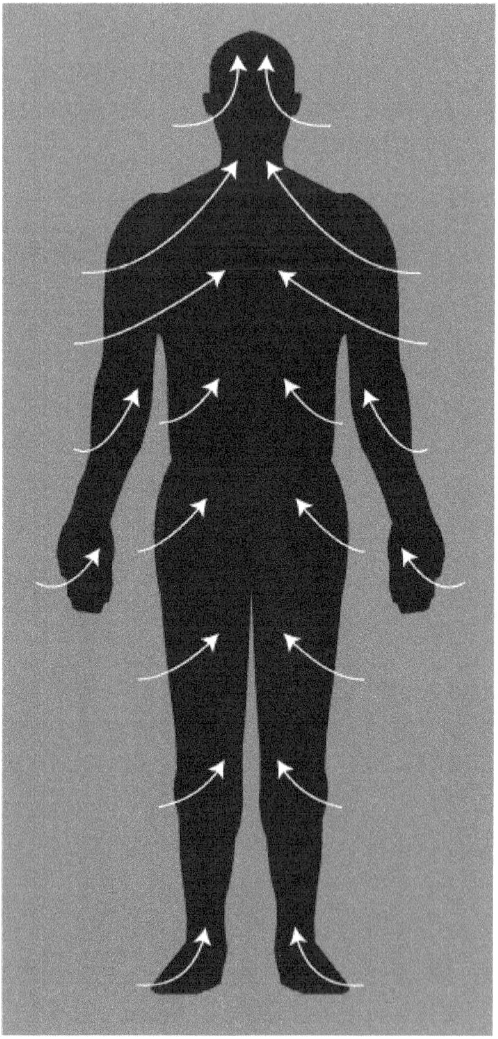

- *Gather the feelings in the psyche so that they are stationary and positioned without moving here and there.*

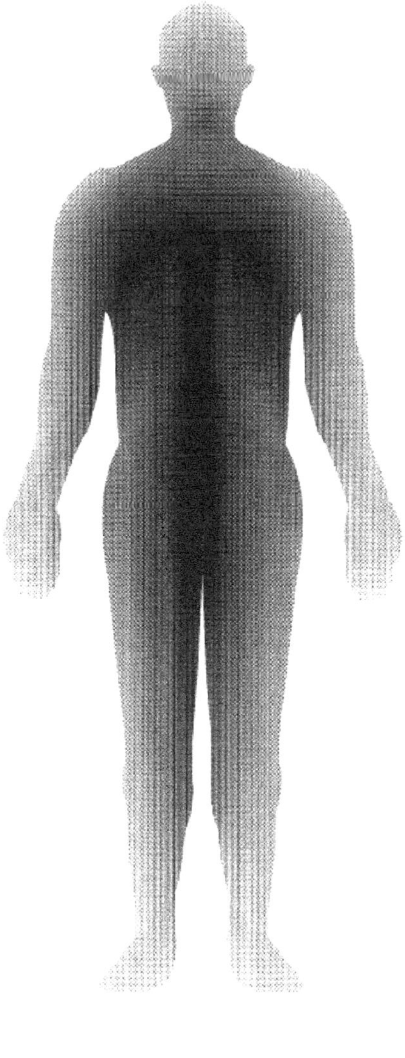

- *Diffuse the stationary energy, so that the feelings become stirred.*
- *If the feelings remain neutral, exert yourself to move the sensations outwards towards the membrane. They may move even in the neutral state.*

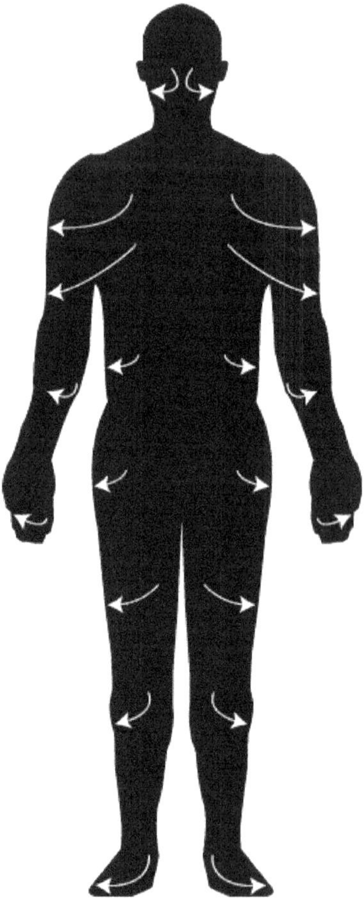

This process of focusing on a sense faculty is done using what Patanjali terms as samyama, which is the three highest stages of yoga as one sequential event. The term samyama is translated as meditation but the meaning must tally with what Patanjali described in the Yoga Sutras.

There he listed dharana focal interest, dhyana effortless focal interest, and samadhi continuous focal interest, as samyama when these three practices flow one into the other in progression or digression.

Mathematically it is:

***dharana + dhyana + samadhi = samyama***

When there is a focal interest which becomes effortless and which in turn becomes continuous for a time; that is meditation practice. This is a process which can be applied to various aspects of existence. In the third chapter of the Yoga Sutras, Patanjali gave several examples of the application of this samyama meditation process.

There is an evolution in this process. There is also a devolution. There is a tightening of the process and a slackening of it. When it is successfully done it may happen so rapidly that the yogi may interpret that he reaches samadhi without doing dharana and dhyana but in fact that is not possible. Similarly when in samadhi the yogi might feel that he was abruptly shifted out of it but actually he has to devolve from samadhi into dhyana and then in dharana. It is a question of the rapidity or slowness of the shifts from one state to another. If it is very rapid, the yogi may fail to observe it and thus will not admit it.

Let us try to understand this at least theoretically. Later we can practice and discover the facts.

If you apply your interest to a reality, any reality, even a physical one, and if you do so thoroughly, then that investment may develop into something which seems to be natural. This means that your mind will no longer be resistant to the application of your interest and will promote it. When you apply yourself in the future, you may find that you can do so effortlessly.

In other words a little attempt to apply your interest will convert into the mind doing everything for you. As people say about practical things, practice makes perfect or that if you repeatedly do something, eventually it will become a reflex. It will become instinctive or reflexive.

As you practice more and more, you will become proficient. You will be able to do that for some time easily. This process is an evolution. In the beginning you were only at the stage of endeavor. When you did a certain amount of effort, that endeavor converted into spontaneity but only for short periods of time. Then as that happens more and more the spontaneity continues for longer periods of time.

The effort stage which is where you began is similar to dharana meditation. The first state of spontaneity is comparable to the dhyana stage. The length spontaneity is like the samadhi stage.

The process is called samyama by Patanjali, which is the rough equivalent of our English term of meditation.

There is a slight difference however, in that in physical skills, usually once you acquire the skill you keep performing at that level. We experience this with athletes who master a game. We witness this with persons who develop skills like carpentry or painting.

It is different in meditation because the yogi must return to using the mind in the usual materialistic way. This is necessary because the physical body functions in a three dimensional environment which has stationary laws of physics which we must comply with.

In meditation once the person evolves from effortful focus to momentary effortless focus and then to timely effortless focus, he or she must, by necessity, unwind from that, just to live as a physical body.

When one reaches samadhi, one must wind down to dhyana. That in turn must change back to dharana. Then the person is released from the focus and finds himself or herself in the conventional awareness on the physical level.

While there are three stages for achieving samyama or meditation, there at least five (5) stages for entering meditation successful and then leaving it to resume conventional awareness.

Notice the term at least. This is because some of us may do additional disciplines to achieve the focus stage. Thus for those students it is more than five stages but it includes those five processes.

The five stages are:

- *effortful focus*
- *momentary effortless focus*
- *timely effortless focus*
- *momentary effortless focus*
- *effortful focus*

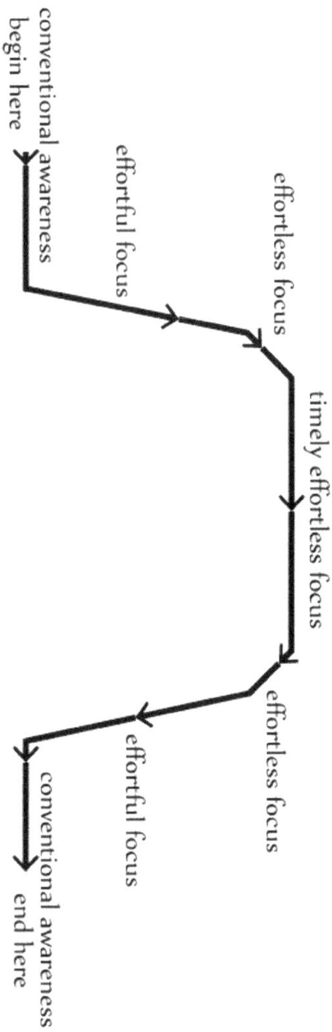


In the diagram, the yogi begins meditation from the conventional awareness of the mind. He makes effortful focus. That evolves into effortless focus, which evolves into timely effortless focus. At this point he is at the peak of the session. From that peak he experiences a descent into momentary effortless focus, which devolves into effortful focus which dissolves leaving him where he began with conventional nature-given awareness.

In some meditations, the yogi may not achieve the timely effortless focus. He may only achieve the effortless focus momentarily.

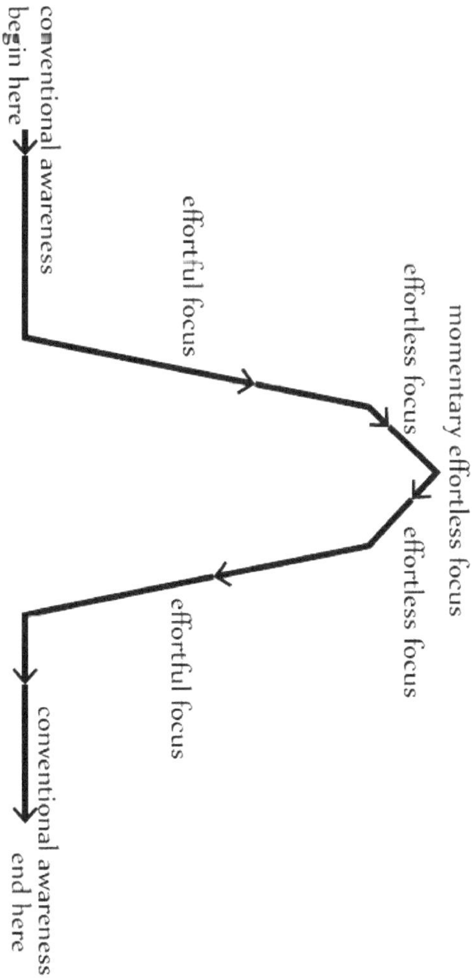

In the diagram above, the yogi never experiences the spontaneous effortless focus except for a moment. This is what happens. He begins with the conventional awareness. From there he applies effortful focus for a sustained period of time. There occurs a short period of effortless focus but as he begins to appreciate it, it reaches a momentary peak, where he loses it and tries to hold fast to it. He finds himself doing the effortful focus again but it devolves into the conventional awareness which is the gift of nature to him.

Some beginners may reach the effortful focus and not advance a step further. This is due to the unruly nature of the mind.

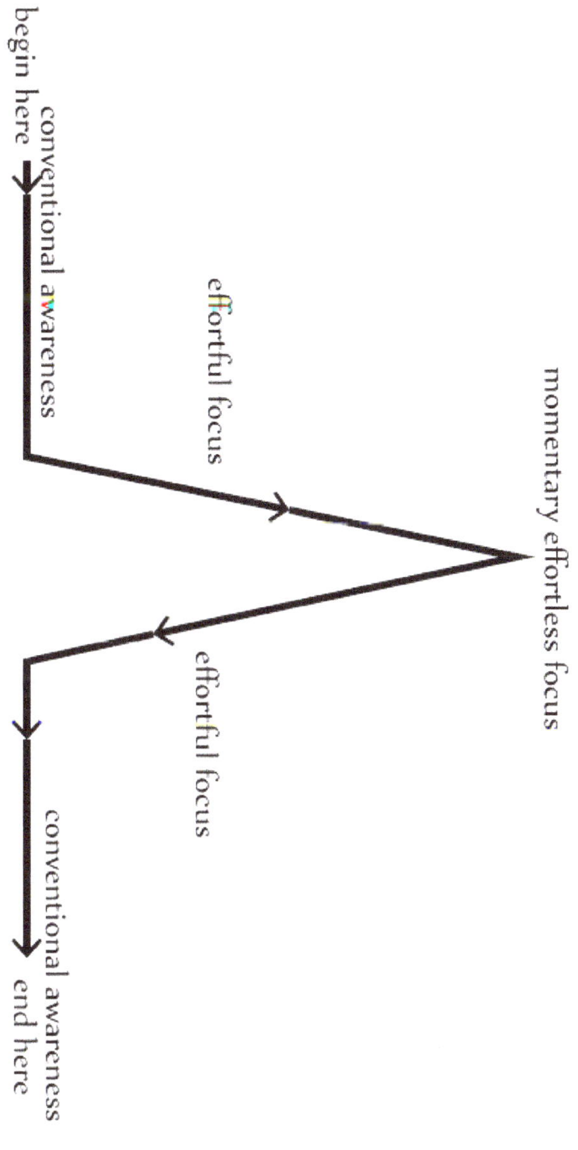


In the diagram above there is a single moment for effortless focus or there may be none of it during the session. The novice yogi begins with the conventional awareness. Then attains an effortful focus but when the effortless focus happens it is for a fleeting moment which appears to be no occurrence to the yogi. After a time doing the session the yogi finds his grip on the effortful focus slipping. Then he discovers himself with the conventional awareness having lost grip in the meditation session.

Others will achieve even less where they will struggle only at the fifth stage of yoga which is pratyahar sensual energy withdrawal. Their entire meditation session will involve that struggle. They will not focus even momentarily on prescribed events of a transcendental value.

When the fight with the mind ends with the mind being silent, with its thoughts and ideas ceased, then meditation can begin in earnest but that is not an easy achievement for everyone who does meditation.

- *Sit to meditate.*
- *Focus yourself on the touch sensation which is everywhere in the body in every cell on every part of every living membrane. Keep your interest on that focus for a time. Do not be discouraged by the neutral feelings. Keep the focus.*

# Chapter 7

# Hearing Sense Focus

In each chapter, the harnessing of the interest of the observing-self is stressed. That is key to this practice. Each lesson involves the application of the unmixed interest of the observer. As nature would have it, the observer usually uses a mixed interest which prejudices his conclusions. If the interest is withdrawn and held in confinement near to the observer, it may derive neutrality, which would certify that the observer receives unbiased observation. This would in turn give the observing-self greater autonomy.

In this chapter we focus on the subtlest sense faculty which is hearing. So far we accessed the neutral stage of the smelling, tasting, seeing and touching. The hearing is the last sense under consideration. By now, you should realize that besides these five senses there is a primal application of the bare energy of the core-self which is its interest.

In the yoga books these psychic or abstract organs in the subtle body are termed as antahkarana which in the literal sense means inner (antah) cause (karana). It is usually defined as a combination of fours aspects of ahamkara, buddhi, manas and chitta. Ahamkara is literally I, (aham) the actor (kara). Buddhi is the intellect, the calculative faculty. Manas is the container which is the mind. It is a mental compartment. Chitta is the emotional energy in the psyche. It can be random or organized, focused or diffused.

For this practice we focus on the ahamkara or sense of identity but in its realized form which is the interest of the observing self. We left aside the buddhi intellect instrument because Patanjali in the Yoga Sutras instructed that it be neglected for the purpose of yoga.

Patanjali wrote this as the second of his sutras:

योगश्चित्तवृत्तिनिरोधः ॥२॥

yogaḥcittavṛtti nirodhaḥ

*yogaḥ – the skill of yoga; cittavṛtti = citta – mento-emotional energy + vṛtti – vibrational mode; nirodhaḥ – cessation, restraint, non-operation.*

**The skill of yoga is demonstrated by the conscious non-operation of the vibrational modes of the mento-emotional energy. (Yoga Sutras 1.2)**

The sense of identity is realized as a person's original interest before that energy is fused into a particular sense. This fusion is mostly involuntary. The selective application of the interest-energy is rarely achieved by a limited entity. Through meditation we may get opportunities to control the fusion but in our day to day lives, it is mostly spontaneously done on the basis of the instincts of the particular species we inhabit.

Let us investigate the neutral hearing sense:

- *Sit to meditate.*
- *Listen for sounds inside the head.*
- *Ignore sounds like digestion and air movements which are inside the trunk of the body.*
- *Listen inside the head.*
- *There is a high pitched or low pitched screeching sound which is heard in the head.*
- *Listen to that sound.*
- *If you do not hear that sound, press a finger from each hand to the outer ear lobes to close them.*

- *This will cause you to hear a rumbling sound in the head.*
- *Listen to that sound for about five (5) minutes.*
- *Release your finger, then listen for a residual sound.*
- *There is a residual sound which will be a high or low pitched frequency which is either quiet or loud. Listen to it.*
- *If you lose track of this sound, you should press the ear lobes again so that you hear the rumbling sound. Keep pressing for a bit until you feel satisfied that your attention has shifted into that sound and has left aside everything else.*
- *Hold to that sound.*
- *Release your fingers. Do as you did before to listen for the background residual sound. Once you hear it listen to that sound. If you do not hear it, again press the ear lopes from the outside and listen to the rumbling sound.*
- *Release your fingers and hear the residual sound. If you still do not hear it, agree with yourself that the sound is there as suggested but you do not hear it.*
- *If there is no residual sound, then listen to the soundless space in your head. That soundlessness is sound. Listen to it.*

Pressing the earlobes as suggested causes the mind to understand that the head space is a special compartment which is a real psychic container. Please adapt to this understanding. As soon as you move the physical and/or subtle bodies you are moving that head space, here or there. You carry it wherever you go. When the subtle body is separated from the physical one, that head space goes with the subtle body. When the subtle body is interspaced with the physical one, that head space coincides with the physical brain and feels as if it is that organ.

The tone of high pitched frequency which is heard in the subtle head may sound like crickets or as a blend of frequencies mixed and resonating. If you do not hear it and if you only have a hollow emptiness in your head, then that hollowness is the objective of this meditation.

- *Sit to meditate.*
- *Using fingers press your earlobes to close them from outside sounds.*
- *Hold the fingers for the count of thirty (30).*
- *Release the fingers.*
- *Listen to the residual or hollow sound which is in the head.*
- *Pull energy from the right and left towards the observing self.*

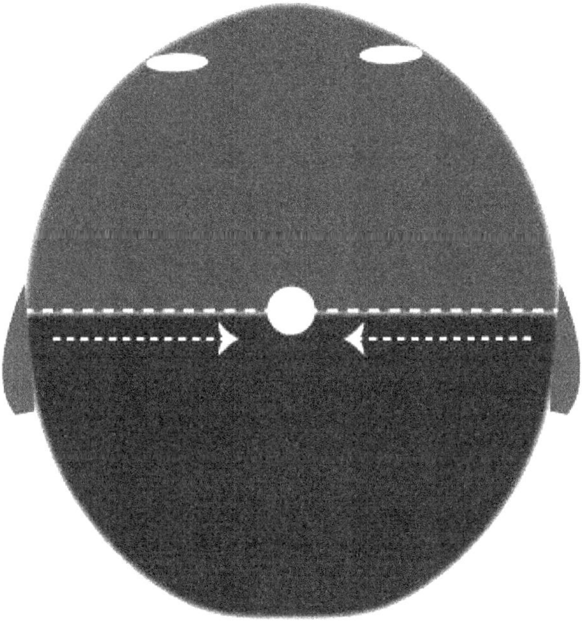

- *Keep pulling energy until you feel the need to relax the pull.*

- *Place the interest-energy through the space at the back of the head, while pulling energy from the back in a loop as in this diagram*

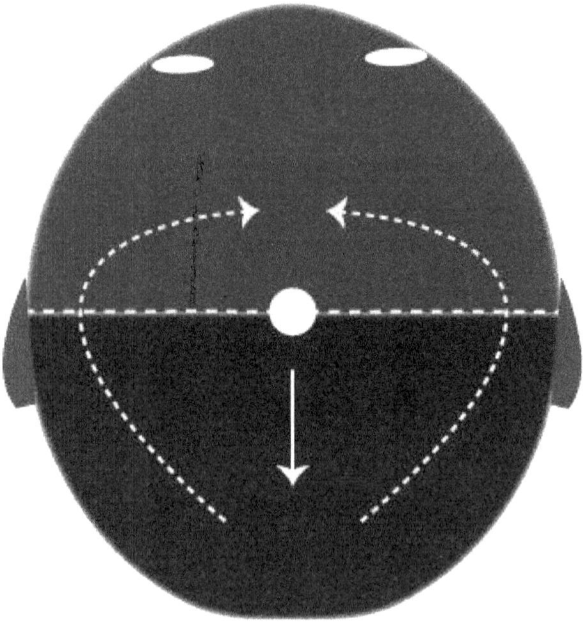

- *Sit to meditate.*
- *Listen for the inner sound in the head or listen to the hollowness in the head.*
- *Focus on that sound or hollowness.*

- *Maintain the focus. Listen with great care to the high pitched frequency, hollowness or low pitched resonance. Listen attentively.*
- *Investigate for any nodes or zones where the sound is more intense or where the hollow is even hollower.*
- *Go to such areas.*
- *Be like a person in a hollow chamber listening to nothing but the sound or hollow of the space around you*

If you see anything or if you happen to visualize anything accidentally, make note of it. That perception is a psychic perception. Once when doing this practice, Michael saw a nude woman. Such vision is clairvoyance. One may also hear a voice or voices. That is clairaudience.

The perception of a nude woman does not necessarily mean that the woman was nude. In some of these perceptions, the subtle body does not see physical or subtle clothing. Hence it sees everything else. Astral vision has phases where one sees through clothing or does not perceive it.

Instances of clairaudience may occur during any of these practice, whereby one clearly hears another person speaking. This person may be thousands of miles away but one will hear the speech as if that person was near.

Such instances are not controlled by the meditator. It happens according to the phase of consciousness which the subtle body experiences at the same time.

Among yogis, the frequency sound or hollowness in the head is termed as naad sound resonance. It is a recommended object of meditation. The practice of collecting, isolation and then reapplying the interest-energy is termed by Patanjali as samyama, which has meditation as its English equivalent.

Here is a related statement from the Yoga Sutras:

श्रोत्राकाशयोः सम्बन्धसंयमाद्दिव्यं श्रोत्रम् ॥४२॥

śrotra ākāśayoḥ saṁbandha saṁyamāt divyaṁ śrotram

*śrotra – hearing sense; ākāśayoḥ – of space; saṁbandha – relationship; saṁyamāt – from the complete restraint of the mento-emotional energy; divyaṁ – divine, supernatural; śrotram – hearing sense.*

**By the complete restraint of the mento-emotional energy, while focusing on the hearing sense and space, a yogin develops supernatural and divine hearing. (Yoga Sutras 3.42)**

This means that if one can apply the unmixed isolated interest-energy to the hearing faculty and the existential space around the observing self, one will in time, develop astral and spiritual clairaudience.

Consider what Patanjali said about the application of the unmixed isolated interest energy. He termed it as samyama.

देशबन्धश्चित्तस्य धारणा ॥१॥

deśa bandhaḥ cittasya dhāraṇā

*deśa – location; bandhaḥ – confinement, restriction; cittasya – of the mento-emotional energy; dhāraṇā – linking of the attention to a concentration force or person.*

**Linking of the attention to a concentration force or person, involves a restricted location in the mento-emotional energy. (Yoga Sutras 3.1)**

तत्र प्रत्ययैकतानता ध्यानम् ॥२॥

tatra pratyayaḥ ekatānatā dhyānam

*tatra – there, in that location; pratyayaḥ – conviction or belief as mental content, instinctive interest; ekatānatā – one continuous threadlike flow of attention = eka – one + tānatā – thread of fiber; dhyānam – effortless linking of the attention to a higher concentration force or person.*

**When in that location, there is one continuous threadlike flow of one's instinctive interest; that is the effortless linking of the attention to a higher concentration force or person. (Yoga Sutras 3.2)**

तदेवार्थमात्रनिर्भासं स्वरूपशून्यमिव समाधिः ॥३॥

tadeva arthamātranirbhāsaṁ
svarūpaśūnyam iva samādhiḥ

*tadeva = tat – that + eva – only, alone; artha – purpose objective; mātra – only, merely; nirbhāsaṁ – illuminating; svarūpa – own form; śūnyam – empty, void, lacking; iva – as if; samādhiḥ – continuous effortless linking of the attention to a higher concentration force or person.*

**That same effortless linkage of the attention when experienced as illumination of the higher concentration force or person, while the yogi feels as if devoid of himself, is *samādhi* or continuous effortless linkage of his attention to the special person, object, or force. (Yoga Sutras 3.3)**

त्रयमेकत्र संयमः ॥४॥

trayam ekatra saṁyamaḥ

*trayam – three; ekatra – in one place, all taken together as one practice; saṁyamah – complete restraint.*

**The three as one practice are the complete restraint. (Yoga Sutras 3.4)**

तज्जयात्प्रज्ञालोकः ॥५॥

tajjayāt prajñālokaḥ

*taj = tad = tat – that; jayāt – from the mastery; prajñā – insight; ālokaḥ – illuminating.*

**From the mastery of that complete restraint of the mento-emotional energy, one develops the illuminating insight. (Yoga Sutras 3.5)**

तस्य भूमिषु विनियोगः ॥६॥

tasya bhūmiṣu viniyogaḥ

*tasya – of it, of this; bhūmiṣu – in stages; viniyogaḥ – application, employment, practice.*

**The practice of this complete restraint occurs in stages. (Yoga Sutras 3.6)**

This means that the withdrawal of the attention of the observing-self and its confinement and then controlled application develops over time in meditation practice. It will yield for the yogi illuminating insight (prajñālokaḥ).

Regarding the interest-energy itself. Patanjali informed us of this:

सत्त्वपुरुषयोरत्यन्तासङ्कीर्णयोः प्रत्ययाविशेषो भोगः
परार्थत्वात्स्वार्थसंयमात्पुरुषज्ञानम्॥३६॥

sattva puruṣayoḥ atyantāsaṁkīrṇayoḥ
pratyayaḥ aviśeṣaḥ bhogaḥ parārthatvāt
svārthasaṁyamāt puruṣajñānam

*sattva – intelligence energy of material nature; puruṣayoḥ – of the individual spirit; atyanta – excessively, extremely, very; asaṁkīrṇayoḥ – of what is distinct or separate; pratyayaḥ – mental content, awareness within the psyche; aviśeṣaḥ – not distinct, inability to distinguish; bhogaḥ – experience; parārthatvāt – what is apart from another thing; svārtha – one own, self interest; saṁyamāt – from the complete restraint of the mento-emotional energy; puruṣa – individual spirit; jñānam – knowledge.*

**Experience results from the inability to distinguish between the individual spirit and the intelligence energy of material nature, even though they are very distinct. By complete restraint of the mento-emotional energy while focusing on self-interest distinct from the other interest, a yogi gets knowledge of the individual spirit. (Yoga Sutras 3.36)**

In this application the interest energy; becomes the object of focus. First it is withdrawn from any and all concerns. Then it is confined by the observing-self and is kept near to that self. Then it is applied to itself by the observer.

In this book we investigated the neutral phase of each of the five senses of smelling, tasting, seeing, touching and hearing. However the handler of these senses is the interest energy. A yogi should go further to investigate it using the procedures we explained herein.

# Index

## M



## N



## O



## P

## U,V,W,X,Y,Z

# *Authors*

***Michael Beloved*** (Yogi Madhvāchārya) introduced the inSelf Yoga™ kundalini and meditation procedure. He first charted the basic mind diagrams and published them in the book *Meditation Pictorial.*

This is for mastery of the 5th stage of yoga, pratyāhāra sensual energy withdrawal, for concentration of soul power and shift of focus to transcendental planes of existence.

Michael designed, used, and tested these methods on the basis of meditation instructions received from several yoga teachers and from the information in the *Bhagavad Gitā, Uddhava Gitā,* and *Anu Gitā, Hatha Yoga Pradipika* and the *Yoga Sūtras of Patanjali.*

**devaPriya Yogini** (Erinn Earth) is a Yoga Educator. Yoga is an ancient science of introspection, psychological purification and ultimate, effortless togetherness with the Supreme Person through meditation.

After graduating from Quincy University in 1996 with a degree in Psychology, devaPriya discovered Yoga as the greatest of humanities psychological studies. Practicing the 8 steps of yoga shed a bright light on the nature of existence and inspired a deeper understanding of reincarnation.

Yoga teaching began in 2000 after formal training at the Sivananda Ashram in the Laurentian Mountains of Quebec. Here, she lived in a tent and studied with monks, engaged in yoga austerities. In 2013 she began training with inSelf Yoga™ master, Michael Beloved in breath infusion for subtle body transformation, a form of kundalini hatha yoga.

# *Publications*

## inSelf Yoga™ Courses

inSelf Yoga™ is the ashtanga process of complete transformation of the psyche of a yogi. Its syllabus was given by Patanjali Mahayogin in the Yoga Sutras. It has physical and psychological applications and reins in the lifestyle of the ascetic.

Core-Self Discovery

**Core-Self Discovery** is the pictorial format of the inSelf Yoga™ course for discovering the core-self in the psyche of the individual soul. This was adapted from Michael Beloved's *Meditation Pictorial* book. These mind diagrams give graphic depiction of what may take place in the head of the subtle body during meditations for pin-pointing the core-self, the observing transcendental I-identity.

This publication is available in paperback, eBook and DVD formats.

Meditation ~ Sense Faculty

Meditation ~ Sense Faculty is the pictorial format of the inSelf Yoga™ course for discovering the psychic sense faculties. This was developed by devaPriya Yogini and concluded by Michael Beloved, who tested the techniques. These mind diagrams give graphic depiction of what may take place in the head of the subtle body during meditations for pin-pointing, isolating and directing the interest energy of the core-self, the observing transcendental I-identity.

## Commentaries

Yoga Sutras of Patanjali

Meditation Expertise

Krishna Cosmic Body

Bhagavad Gita Explained

Anu Gita Explained

Kriya Yoga Bhagavad Gita

Brahma Yoga Bhagavad Gita

Uddhava Gita Explained

Kundalini Hatha Yoga Pradipika

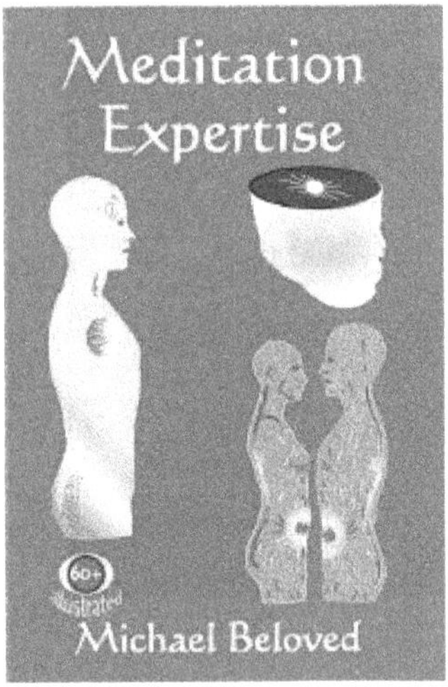

**Yoga Sutras of Patanjali** is the globally acclaimed text book of yoga. This has detailed expositions of yoga techniques. Many kriya techniques are vividly described in the commentary.

**Meditation Expertise** is an analysis and application of the Yoga Sutras. This book is loaded with illustrations and has detailed explanations of secretive advanced meditation techniques which are called kriyas in the Sanskrit language.

**Krishna Cosmic Body** is a narrative commentary on the Markandeya Samasya portion of the Aranyaka Parva of the Mahabharata. This is the detailed description of the dissolution of the world, as experienced by the great yogin Markandeya who transcended the cosmic deity, Brahma, and reached Brahma's source who is a divine infant Krishna.

**Bhagavad Gita Explained** shows what was said in the Gita without religious overtones and sectarian biases.

**Anu Gita Explained** is the detailed description of the effect-energy of current actions in application to future lives.

**Kriya Yoga Bhagavad Gita** shows the instructions for those who are doing kriya yoga.

**Brahma Yoga Bhagavad Gita** shows the instructions for those who are doing brahma yoga.

**Uddhava Gita Explained** shows the instructions to Uddhava which are more advanced than the ones given to Arjuna.

Bhagavad Gita is an instruction for applying the expertise of yoga in the cultural field. This is why the process taught to Arjuna is called karma yoga which means karma + yoga or cultural activities done with a yogic demeanor.

Uddhava Gita is an instruction for applying the expertise of yoga to attaining spiritual status. This is why it is explains jnana yoga and bhakti yoga in detail. Jnana yoga is using mystic skill for knowing the spiritual part of existence. Bhakti yoga is for developing affectionate relationships with divine beings.

Karma yoga is for negotiating the social concerns in the material world and therefore it is inferior to bhakti yoga which concerns negotiating the social concerns in the spiritual world.

This world has a social environment and the spiritual world has one too.

Right now Uddhava Gita is the most advanced informative spiritual book on the planet. There is nothing anywhere which is superior to it or which goes into so much detail as it. It verified that historically Krishna is the most advanced human being to ever have left literary instructions on this planet. Even Patanjali Yoga Sutras which I translated and gave an application for in my book, **Meditation Expertise,** does not go as far as the Uddhava Gita.

Some of the information of these two books is identical but while the Yoga Sutras are concerned with the personal spiritual emancipation (kaivalyam) of the individual spirits, the Uddhava Gita explains that and also explains the situations in the spiritual universes.

Bhagavad Gita is from the *Mahabharata* which is the history of the Pandavas. Arjuna, the student of the Gita, is one of the Pandavas brothers. He was in a social hassle and did not know how to apply yoga expertise to solve it.

Krishna gave him a crash-course on the battlefield about that.

Uddhava Gita is from the *Srimad Bhagavatam (Bhagavata Purana),* which is a history of the incarnations of Krishna. Uddhava was a relative of Krishna. He was concerned about the situation of the deaths of many of his relatives but Krishna diverted Uddhava's attention to the practice of yoga for the purpose of successfully migrating to the spiritual environment.

**Kundalini Hatha Yoga Pradipika** is perhaps the most detailed commentary, most English-expressed translation of the Hatha Yoga Pradipika with profuse illustrations of what happens in the subtle body of a yogi who is proficient in kundalini manipulation for subtle body transformation. Some diagrams show what happens in the subtle body of a yogi who masters this process.

The tantric aspects of controlled psyche-arresting sexual intercourse is plainly discusses just as Swatmarama Mahayogin did in the Sanskrit original but with more details in the commentary of exactly how that is done. This is the theory. A reader is responsible for the practice but there is sufficient exposition. Any ascetic can use this information to develop a kundalini yoga practice. The raja yoga integration of remaining introverted while being externally occupied is explained.

## Explained Series

Bhagavad Gita Explained

Anu Gita Explained

Uddhava Gita Explained

The speciality of these books is that they are free of missionary intentions, cult tactics and philosophical distortion. Instead of using these books to add credence to a philosophy, meditation process, belief or plea for followers, I spread the information out so that a reader can look through this literature and freely take or leave anything as desired.

When Krishna stressed himself as God, I stated that. When Krishna laid no claims for supremacy, I showed that. The reader is left to form an independent opinion about the validity of the information and the credibility of Krishna.

There is a difference in the discourse with Arjuna in the Bhagavad Gita and the one with Uddhava in the Uddhava Gita. In fact these two books may appear to contradict each other. In the Bhagavad Gita, Krishna pressured Arjuna to complete social duties. In the Uddhava Gita, Krishna insisted that Uddhava should abandon the same.

The Anu Gita is completely different to the Bhagavad Gita. Krishna refused to display the Universal Form. He quoted a siddha from a higher dimension who lectured on the effect-energies of actions as these construct a person's future opportunities.

## Meditation Series

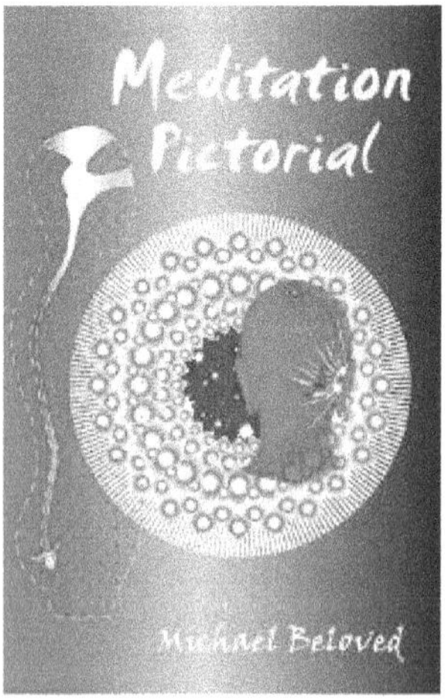


Meditation Pictorial

Meditation Expertise

Meditation ~ Sense Faculty

The speciality of these books is the mind diagrams which profusely illustrate what is written. This shows exactly what one has to do mentally to develop and then sustain a meditation practice.

In the **Meditation Pictorial**, one is shown how to develop psychic insight, a feature without which meditation is imagination and visualization, without any mystic experience per se.

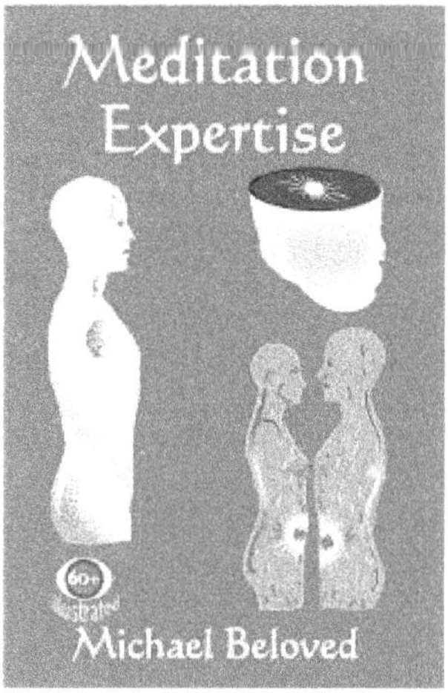


In the **Meditation Expertise**, one is shown how to corral one's practice to bring it in line with the classic syllabus of yoga which Patanjali lays out as the ashtanga yoga 8-staged practice.

Both books are profusely illustrated with mind diagrams showing the components of psychic consciousness and the inner design of the subtle body.

In the **Meditation ~ Sense Faculty** one is shown how to isolate and reapply the interest energy of the observing-self. It is rendered into the neutral state of each of the five sense faculties. The default location of the observing-self is discovered and maintained with all interests withdrawn from other attractions in the psyche.

# Specialty Topics

sex you!

The mystery of sex and reincarnation is explained in detail, not in terms of religion or superstition but by psychic facts which any individual can observe, if he or she can shift focus to the psychic plane. Books like the Bardo Thodol (Tibetan Book of the Dead) and the Egyptian Book of the Dead (Papyrus of Ani), along with Bhagavad Gita, the reincarnation teaching of Buddha and other vital books, took humanity through a spiritual technological leap through time into the hereafter. Perhaps none of these texts dealt with the incidences of sex and reincarnation head on, especially the link between you and the sexual act of your parents which produced your body. In this book you get the details in plain terms without mystery and religious impositions.

Spiritual Master

Practically every positive and negative aspect of having a guru is discussed in this book with recommendations of how to deal with gurus safely. A non-proficient guru can be useful despite his faults, but one must know how to side-step hassles and get to the business at hand, which is to get effective techniques from a spiritual master.

In some cases the spiritual master will be a complete fraud but one should not let that deter one from making spiritual progress in his association. “But why,” one might ask, “should one stay with a fraudulent guru?” The answer is that if providence puts one in that position, one should honor providence but one should do so without getting hurt by the unqualified spiritual master. This and similar topics are discussed in this book.

Masturbation Psychic Details:

--- A short paper about the psychic side of a masturbation event with a tour through the possibilities of possession by departed spirits who access the form of the physical actor. Everything points to the masturbator, until we consider the content energy of the sexual urge to see if it has another person force as its primal gusher.

What would happen if a hereafter person(s) in the urge were evacuated from it? Would the physical actor suddenly lose the impetus and become reluctant to bring the body to climax?

# English Series

Bhagavad Gita English

Anu Gita English

Markandeya Samasya English

Yoga Sutras English

Uddhava Gita English

Hatha Yoga Pradipika English

One of these books is the **Hatha Yoga Pradipika English**. that is the translations of Swatmarama's classic detailed thesis about Nath Yoga or Hatha Yoga which is in fact not asana-posture yoga alone but kundalini yoga manipulation for subtle body transformation. For a detailed commentary please see our volume appropriately as Kundalini Hatha Yoga Pradipika.

My suggestion is that you read Bhagavad Gita English, the Anu Gita English, the Markandeya Samasya English, the Yoga Sutras English and lastly the Uddhava Gita English, which is much more complicated and detailed.

For each of these books we have at least one commentary, which is published separately. Thus your particular interest can be researched further in the commentaries.

The smallest of these commentaries and perhaps the simplest is the one for the Anu Gita. We published its commentary as the Anu Gita Explained. The Bhagavad Gita explanations were published in three distinct targeted commentaries. The first is Bhagavad Gita Explained, which sheds lights on how people in the time of Krishna and Arjuna regarded the information and applied it. Bhagavad Gita is an exposition of the application of yoga practice to cultural activities, which is known in the Sanskrit language as karma yoga.

Interestingly, Bhagavad Gita was spoken on a battlefield just before one of the greatest battles in the ancient world. A warrior, Arjuna, lost his wits and had no idea that he could apply his training in yoga to political dealings. Krishna, his charioteer, lectured on the spur of the moment to give Arjuna the skill of using yoga proficiency in cultural dealings including how to deal with corrupt officials on a battlefield.

The second commentary is the Kriya Yoga Bhagavad Gita. This clears the air about Krishna's information on the science of kriya yoga, showing that its techniques are clearly described free of charge to anyone who takes the time to read Bhagavad Gita. Kriya yoga concerns the battlefield which is the psyche of the living being. The internal war and the mental and emotional forces which are hostile to self realization are dealt with in the kriya yoga practice.

The third commentary is the Brahma Yoga Bhagavad Gita. This shows what Krishna had to say outright and what he hinted about which concerns the brahma yoga practice, a mystic process for those who mastered kriya yoga.

There is one commentary for the **Markandeya Samasya English**. The title of that publication is Krishna Cosmic Body.

There are two commentaries to the Yoga Sutras. One is the Yoga Sutras of Patanjali and the other is the Meditation Expertise. These give detailed explanations of the process of Yoga.

For the Uddhava Gita, we published the Uddhava Gita Explained. This is a large book and requires concentration and study for integration of the information. Of the books which deal with transcendental topics, my opinion is that the discourse between Krishna and Uddhava has the complete information about the realities in existence. This book is the one which removes massive existential ignorance.

# *Online Resources*

## Visit the Websites and Forum

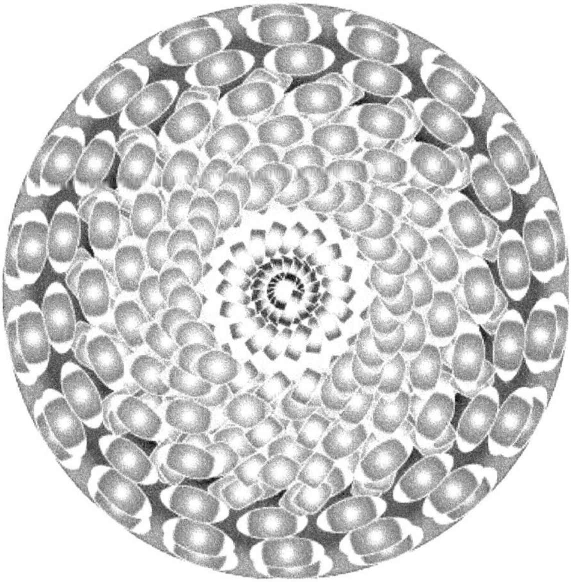

***Email:*** *michaelbelovedbooks@gmail.com*

*axisnexus@gmail.com*

*devapriyayogini@gmail.com*

***Websites:*** *michaelbeloved.com*

*inselfyoga.net*

***Forum:*** inselfyoga.com